MANAGING YOUR BUILD

Extend • Restore • Renovate • New Build

MANAGING YOUR BUILD

Extend • Restore • Renovate • New Build

Andrew Stanway

Stobart Davies Ltd

Published: 2009 by Stobart Davies Limited
Stobart House, Pontyclerc
Penybanc Road, Ammanford
Carmarthenshire SA18 3HP, UK
www.stobartdavies.com

British Library Cataloguing in Publication Data
A CIP record for this book is available from the British Library

ISBN: 978-1-85442-141-1

Typesetting and design by: Stobart Davies Ltd, Ammanford

Front cover design and drawings: Marcus Patton

Printed by: Cromwell Press Group, Trowbridge, Wiltshire

Contents

Introduction

I came into project management by a highly unorthodox route. After qualifying in medicine in the late 1960s and working as a doctor for some years, I ran a medical publishing house and later my own medical film company, producing documentaries for distribution around the world. As a young man running a highly successful international business I soon realised how much I enjoyed the delivery of complex projects. And film-making is about the most complex type of project there is. Just look at the credits at the end of any feature film and ask yourself how all these people are sourced, motivated, managed, financed, and empowered to deliver their skills and passion. This is the job of the producer (project manager).

In fact, one of the world's leading project managers claims that the motion picture industry can teach everyone something about the subject.

The nature of film-making is, after all, a way of working that has a one-off opportunity to get things right. This cannot be said of many large-scale endeavours. The few minutes of film scheduled for that day have to happen, which means that film producers simply have to get the job done on time and on budget. And this is a task that could involve hundreds of people on any one day!

Even with my relatively small company, I still faced the same challenges: getting the script right; managing the medical politics; getting the 'stars' and crew in the right place at the right time; transporting, feeding and accommodating everybody, often in foreign countries; dealing with strongly-held opinions, experts and big egos; satisfying unions; hiring equipment; fighting crises; coping with bad weather; illness; and pressure from the clients; filming the same shots on the same day in a variety of ways for each different country's eventual requirements; emotions everywhere; and so on. The director of a film steers the ship in creative terms – but he would simply be unable to do his job without the producer building the 'canvas' on which he could 'paint'.

I then spent more than twenty years as a psychotherapist, during which time I had the honour of listening to large numbers of people from all walks of life. Some of these were managers, and a few were very successful indeed. I started asking myself what it was about these highly successful 'deliverers' of projects that made them so special.

The answer was simple....they were 'people' people, who knew how to listen, and thus how to manage effectively. Because I was so impressed by this I started a series of courses in listening skills, some residential over several days, for individuals, couples, and even government personnel departments. Time and again the subsequent feedback was that the attendees had become better managers. Yet I had taught them nothing overtly about 'managing' or 'management'. What they learned was how to listen. It was this that made all the difference.

I've been involved in building all my life. I even worked part-time in a timber yard through my teens. My father was a senior manager in a major international construction company. And one thing I've noticed about the building trades, and the construction industry in general, is that not a lot of listening goes on. Is it any wonder then, that so many projects, from airports to Mrs Jones' extension, go so woefully wrong? I started as a hands-on, part-time, builder in my twenties and now, nearly forty years later, I'm still learning about the industry and about people. And this is hardly surprising. On one large project I employed more than 200 people over a period of a few years.....in contrast with another (concurrent) one that involved the complete gutting of the whole innards (floors and all) of a four-storey, city-centre, property back to the external walls and rebuilding it in just four months.

This said, this is not a book about how actually to build, extend, or renovate a house. There are many publications that'll help you with this, of which Mark Brinkley's *The Housebuilder's Bible* is one of the best. I should also point out that this book is not about building for profit. I'm assuming the work you do will be for yourself and your family, even if it happens to make a profit.

Managing Your Build fills in the gaps that other building books leave and focuses entirely on build management matters. If you employ a builder he'll manage the actual construction elements. But there's far more to building work than this. You will be the overall manager controlling the *project*.

With years of self-building behind me I have, in recent years, been using my 30 years' experience to project-manage and specify builds for others.

Project management as a discipline has, over my lifetime, gone from an intuitive sort of applied common sense, to an academic endeavour. Many of us at the coal face wonder whether such aggrandisement should be a feature of the business, but modern life is like this. There are now huge textbooks on the subject and numerous academics researching and writing away. Many of the largest construction undertakings everywhere around the world are now run by project management companies rather than by architects.

But for all of this, I know that readers of this book will never want to become a part of this esoteric elite – and nor do I – so you'll be relieved to hear you won't even get a sniff of anything but the most basic of project management theories, and I won't expect you to do anything at all on a computer (unless you want to), let alone learn how to use project management software. None of this is necessary at the level you'll need to be effective.

Most people I've asked say that managing their build has taught them a huge amount about life and about themselves and that they've gained skills they can take forward into other areas of their lives. Hopefully, managing the build your own house, conversion, refurbishment or extension will be fun, life-changing and rewarding.

Managing Your Build is on hand to help.

Throughout the book I use the word 'he' as a shorthand for 'he' or 'she'. This not only reflects the fact that the overwhelming majority of those involved domestic building projects are men, but is also easier to read. There are, however, increasing numbers of women in all branches of the construction industry, especially in planning and design.

PART ONE

STARTING AT THE BEGINNING

1 Projects and project management

What is a project?

A project is rather different from most people's experience of work. They do their jobs day after day, trying to satisfy the on-going needs of their employers or their own business.

A project is fundamentally different in that its very success is based on the outcome of a given task. It is thus goal-centred. OK, project managers have to engage intelligently and effectively with the 'process' but what's important is the 'product'. Provided a project is completed in line with what was agreed, how it actually gets to happen is secondary.

All of this means, by definition, that a project has a finite life. Running the customer care department of a car sales company, in contrast, is never-ending. All projects have a beginning, a middle, and an end, at which time the project manager loses his job and has to look for employment again!

This is the nature of project management in every sphere of business and commercial life. And it will be true of your build.

At this point I should acknowledge that individual personalities differ hugely on how suited they are to all this. Some individuals are intrinsically 'process' people and others largely 'product' centred. If what you like is being part of a team that works away in the background to produce results over a long term, you'll feel very differently about yourself compared with those who are really only happy when up against a deadline, under pressure, aiming for some sort of goal. It is these latter types that find managing projects particularly exciting and rewarding.

However, this doesn't mean that if you are a 'process' person in your daily life you won't be up to managing your build. You may very well be. It could be you've simply never had the opportunity to do so. In fact many 'workers in the vineyard' are there not because they can't do anything else but rather because they've never had a chance to.

What is a project manager?

A project manager is an individual who takes it upon himself (or is appointed) to manage a project. Any of us embarking on a self-build effectively appoints ourselves to this role. Unfortunately, most people doing so haven't a clue what's involved and soon find they have neither the skills, aptitude, nor tools to do the job. Hopefully this book will help.

The thing that makes being a project manager so challenging is that it is a job that involves foretelling the future. Worse still, you then undertake to make that prediction come true! Now add the fact that you undertake to do all

The job of a project manager, whatever he's managing, is to:

- Scope the work (take a detailed look at what's involved)
- Plan what has to happen and when
- Plan what resources will be needed to make it happen
- Assess the risks in the system
- Deal with the day-to-day problems that get in the way of achieving the goal
- Deliver the project on time and on budget to an agreed set of end-points

this for a fixed amount of money, and usually in a fixed amount of time, and you can see how difficult project management is. Given this level of difficulty it makes sense to say to yourself (and to those around you), 'OK, this seems to be a good project, I'll take a look at it and see if it's possible'. I look in detail on page 116 at how to do this.

All sounds easy, doesn't it? 'I want to build a four-bedroom house for my family, this year, using a builder as the main contractor.' This could fairly be said to summarise the above points in the box. But if things were this easy, there'd be no need for a book like this.

In fact, to achieve this apparently simple goal will involve you in between two and three thousand hours of thinking, planning, worry, physical work, phone calls, stress, fear, elation, delight, fulfilment, self-doubt, pressure, and much more.

When I manage a project for a client they understandably express their needs and requirements. This is only fair since they are paying the bills. But when you come to manage your own build, you'll be the client as well as the manager. This is good in many ways but not so great in others.

"What do you think I am....a project manager?"

As a professional project manager I have a much 'cleaner' relationship with my clients than I have with myself when managing a project of my own. When I'm in a professional role, my clients say what they want; will end up living in what we produce in response to this brief and judge how the end result compares with what they envisaged at the start of the project. When building for others I have little say in their taste of house design or finishes, how much they have to spend, and many other variables. I simply take their 'givens' and work with them.

Even very seasoned managers have told me how hard they found their personal build

When you manage your own project, though, you are both manager and client, and this can be hard. First, you'll have no one but yourself to blame for changes in plan, or an unsatisfactory outcome, but more importantly you'll also be much closer emotionally to the project than a professional is when working for a client. This might seem counter-instinctual at first as it would appear that not having a client would be simpler as you're cutting out the middle man. Alas, this isn't what happens in practice. And, paradoxically, even when building apparently just for ourselves we in fact have other 'clients' – or what are known in modern management-speak as 'stakeholders'.

These stakeholders are your family, friends, and even your neighbours. Your workforce too will have their opinions and needs and will thus become stakeholders. In reality, even if you imagine you are building just for yourself, this will rarely be the case, no matter how much you see it as 'your baby'.

This is one of the many hidden agendas that exist every day on self-build sites: agendas that most people neither recognise nor deal with. When working for a client I don't get this. Or if I do, it's at arm's length and in a less personal and emotional way, which makes life easier as it is clear whose business is whose.

Now you can see why it can be so hard to manage your own project....even if you are a good manager in another area of life. Even very seasoned managers say how hard they found their personal build. The construction industry is truly a world of its own. Although most work is done professionally and to a good standard, all too often things can be disappointingly poor, or even unsafe. On occasions the levels of inefficiency and incompetence can be beyond belief to those who have never experienced them. One reason for the low standards is that part, or all, of the construction process takes place out of doors in all weathers, in a temporary 'factory', with a temporary workforce.

Your various stakeholders will all have their (legitimate to them) views; will all have somewhat different notions of what they mean by a successful outcome; and the more stakeholders there are the greater the number of variables there'll be as each tries to influence the system as it progresses. Some of these stakeholders will be your professionals. They will carry most weight when trying to influence your build....and often they'll be right. However, many's the time you'll disagree with them and will have to make brave decisions that are at odds with their professional opinions. This can be very hard indeed but you are the manager and it is you who must eventually take decisions over which you will stand. The bottom line is that it's you who'll be living in the place, not them.

Before I go through the basic work of a project manager and the skills he or she will need when setting up a new build, I think it'll be helpful to spend some time looking in a more general way at what's involved in building. There's little point learning how to manage something when you're not aware of what there is to manage!

2 Building the dream

Most of us creating our dream home, or a serious extension or conversion, are pretty clear what we want....or rather what we'd like. Of course there's nothing wrong with a dream or fantasy as a starting point but very soon this will have to be converted into hard reality. And the reality is that we simply cannot 'have it all', however much we kid ourselves we can.

When working with couples as a therapist I found that sexual, and indeed other, fantasies, rarely lived up to their owner's expectations if acted out. In fact for many, the practical acting out of a favourite fantasy deprives it of its magical powers to excite and please. After all, when we fantasise about any subject, such as a holiday, everything is perfect and nothing

One small step for man...

goes wrong. This is why fantasies are so powerful, enticing and rewarding.

It's much the same with fantasies of our dream home. So how can we retain the power and seduction of the original fantasy yet end up with a realistic, liveable result? After all, there are few worse things than a dream that goes pear-shaped.

The scope, time, cost, quality dilemma

As project managers we need to get an early grip on the issues of scope, time, cost, and quality. It is usually impossible to satisfy all four in any single project...there is no such thing as a fast, cheap, top-quality house build. If you are very skilled and plan well you can, however, almost always get two out of these, and you might even be able to revise the scope a little as you go along. An early task is to decide which of these four is most important to you. Is your dream home to be built to a very tight budget? Is quality your main objective, no matter what the cost or time? Is time of little importance, given you want superb quality yet have little money? Or do you want to remain flexible at every stage so you can alter the scope of the build?

Only you can make these decisions. Once made, though, you have to be big enough to go through with them and to take responsibility for them. Many first-time self-builders have never been asked to make big decisions like this in any area of their life, and it can seem a real burden at first. Take heart from the fact that most people say it gets easier as the build progresses!

Scope

Scoping is the starting point for any new building work. Time spent now is a worthwhile investment in the future of the project. Scoping is the process by which you decide what is included and what is outside the project. Many people make the mistake of cracking on with detailed problem solving and planning before they even get the scope right. Scope is different from needs. You might need a four-bedroom bungalow, or a bigger kitchen but this is not the scope of the project. Even more important, scoping your project involves understanding right from the start what's going to be involved. In a sense I see the process of scoping as creating the road map over which you will travel during your design and build.

Questions you need to be asking – and answering – when getting to grips with the scope of your project include:

- What is your overall objective?
- What, in detail, are you trying to achieve, and how will you know you have achieved it?
- Who will be involved in deciding on matters of cost, quality, schedule and acceptable end points?
- How are you going to manage people's expectations?
- What are the foreseeable risks you're likely to encounter?
- Who, apart from yourself, will actually be making day-to-day decisions?

I'll look in detail at how to do all this on page 116.

When creating your overall objective you'll obviously need to take your family and any other interested parties into account. They too will have their fantasies of what the end result will be. Your professionals, especially your architect, will also want their input. In fact, a good architect who really listens can be very helpful with early scoping.

In my opinion this is the most vital starting point for a new house build, or any major building work, because experience shows that many of those who are most stressed when building have not done this stage well. They lack the overall background 'map' and find themselves wandering around pointless highways and byways fighting design, build, financial, management and emotional fires the whole time. This costs more in time, energy and nerves and can make life horrid for everyone involved in the project.

The problem for many of us it that 'the dream' attains an importance in our minds that all too easily results in sloppy thinking and behaviour. This said, even when I am managing a very expensive and complex project for others I too have to dream. Indeed, were it not for this dream, it would often be impossible to find the spirit to carry on when the going gets exceptionally tough. But, without proper scoping of the project in the first place I would feel vulnerable and unnecessarily stressed out. Having a road map gives everyone a sense of purpose that they can call on when events conspire to wreck everything. Rather like a young child's security blanket, this map gives us confidence that all will be well, even if it seems very unlikely at any one moment!

It isn't just you who'll have 'the dream'

A brief word about managing people's expectations. It isn't just you who'll have 'the dream'. Your family and friends, your builders – and even people who hardly know you – will cherish their versions of your dream. Professional project managers spend a lot of time early on ensuring that all those involved express their expectations. These can then be factored into the overall plan, cost, time, and quality mix until there's a consensus. It'll be much the same for you as the manager of your project. If you don't take responsibility for this at the start you'll be plagued by annoying comments and the risk that people will imagine you have fallen short, whereas in reality you've delivered exactly what was intended. Those around you may need constant re-grounding in this reality or their own fantasies of your project could get in the way of your very tangible and acceptable achievements.

Professional project managers have to address all the issues outlined above – and many more. Many of the questions are fairly easy to answer even if you have little or no previous experience. But the hardest of all to address is probably that of risk assessment. Whole books have been written on the subject, so I can only skim the surface of it here.

Risk assessment. When dreaming about our new project, even if we have a tried-and-tested builder on board – and we may not if we're doing most of it ourselves – it's vital to look ahead and plan for disasters or setbacks.

The question is: what is an acceptable level of risk? This can be hard to ascertain and you'll probably need to seek advice from an engineer, architect, or quantity surveyor. No one can accurately predict the risk caused by bad weather or tricky ground conditions but professionals can certainly tell you about many of the risks that could be avoided. They've seen them all before. It's also important to bear in mind that we all have different personality types that handle risk in various ways. To some, the intrinsic risk of a self-build is what turns them on. To others, the financial risk alone keeps them awake at night.

There are two types of risk when running a project...risks to the project itself and risks to you personally. Managing risks to the project involves pre-planning ways of preventing adverse events in the first place and working out ways of coping in the event that they subsequently occur. This means having well-developed, contingency plans – 'If X happens then I'll do Y and the cost will be Z.' It is vital to have a budget for such contingencies. This can be anything from 10% of the project price on a simple build to 40% or more for a complex refurbishment.

There are two types of risk when running a project...risks to the project itself and risks to you personally

Risks to yourself include personal injury or illness, be it physical or mental; damage to your family relationships; how your job might suffer if you're doing the build alongside paid employment; what your friends and relatives will think; what else you could/should have done with the money; what will happen if the finances go pear-shaped? and so on. Talking all this through with those who care about you, and especially your close family, will help everyone prepare for the undoubted risks that are part of any long-term, expensive, and complex activity. Things will definitely go wrong – sometimes disastrously so. Having your risk assessment strategy planned out will give both you and your family peace of mind.

I look at risks in a lot more detail on page 182.

Time

I always think there's a sort of 'natural time' for a build. Given a particular construction method and management system, builds seem to take about the same time whatever you do – unless you hit very serious problems or are very unlucky or incompetent. Most hands-on self-builders complete the average detached family home within two years. Most professional building companies complete the same-sized project within half this time.

People's ideas about time differ a lot. Some self-builders devote themselves to their project and frankly don't much care how much time it takes. They argue that their time is their own and every hour they spend is one they don't have to pay someone else for! This is good sense provided your time schedule is in line with everyone else's. You might be looking on your build as a super hobby activity that doesn't have to be finished on a particular date, but the rest of your family may not share this view. Neither may your bank manager!

Most of us borrow cash to do our build and so need to be pretty time conscious. Of course there's a happy medium but finding it can be a challenge. Getting everything done fast and well is usually very costly and few of us can take this route. 'Rolls Royce' specialist subcontractors can indeed do certain specialist things in a fraction of the time of your builder or a local subbie but it'll often cost you dearly. Of course there'll be times when it'll pay to splash out to get a particular task done very quickly because the costs involved in holding up other trades could be even higher. This is one of the many management decisions you'll find yourself making as you go along.

Getting foundation and groundwork completed in the good weather, and ensuring the building is watertight by the autumn are two proven end-points that can save money.

Cost

One of the biggest killers of building the dream is running out of cash. Most of us in today's high-expectation world desire more than we can afford. Property programmes on TV and numerous publications keep upping the ante in a way that makes us feel disappointed or even a failure if we can't 'have it all'. But often the truth is we cannot. Setting your sights on realistic outcomes is a vital part of planning the project. You'll probably be able to get a much better quality build than if you were buying from a developer or national house builder but you probably won't be able to get fabulous unless you have loads of money to spend.

> **Setting your sights on realistic outcomes is a vital part of planning the project**

As a broad guide, if a build costs X with you managing and hands-on building virtually everything yourself, it'll cost X +10% to have it project-managed professionally and X + 25-30% to have it built by a contractor. Clearly there are big savings to be made by going the completely self-build route but this assumes you can do it as fast and as well as a builder and that your time really is 'free'. If you could be earning more by doing your day job, then the savings aren't what they appear to be. Of course self-building isn't just about saving money. It can be impossible to value the sense of achievement, the fun, the lessons learned for life, and so on. Whichever route you take *you'll* still end up managing the *project, whoever* manages the actual build.

For most of us the amount of money available for the project is our key limiting factor. We can usually forego some of the quality somewhere

"Hell....is that what I paid for it?"

and many of us can allow time to slip a bit but cash is usually pretty limited no matter how large our budget. There will always be differences of opinion about time and quality but a fixed amount of money isn't a matter for debate. Emotions run high when planning the original budget – or funding over-runs – as family members ask what else could be done if the money weren't being spent on a new home. Discussions about missed holidays, the long-lost dream of a new car, and so on, can make heavy demands on your empathic listening skills (see page 16).

Managing cash flow. This is always going to be a tricky task, given the uncertain nature of so much to do with building. This makes early planning of cash flow requirements a must. It helps to have some cash reserves you can call on in case lenders don't come up trumps when you need them. The most frustrating financial dilemma is where tradesmen refuse to work any more because they haven't yet been paid for work done and your lender won't release more cash until the work *is* done. This Catch 22 is not uncommon, so be prepared to deal with it somehow. It is at times like these that you'll need your 'dream' to keep you going in the wee small hours! For more detail on cash flow, see page 72.

Quality

I've left this till last in talking about the dream house because it is much more subjective than the other variables. In my opinion, a lot of nonsense is talked about quality. Given that the basic structure and fabric of your new home is built to modern standards and regulations, it is possible to buy very good – or more to the point – 'good enough' fixtures,

There will always be differences of opinion about time and quality but a fixed amount of money isn't a matter for debate

fittings and finishes at modest prices. For more on this, see page 167. OK, you won't want your dream home to be fitted out with cheap stuff from the DIY 'sheds' but this isn't necessary any more. As soon as a top-end product becomes available to high-spenders, the mass market alternative, often scarcely perceivable as different, becomes available at a fraction of the cost. Even if you are a terrible snob and it keeps you awake at night, no one else will be able to tell the difference. It has now become a matter of pride to me to source cost-effective alternatives that others imagine cost a fortune. In fact, it is probably easier today than it has ever been cleverly to create a look that fools. Your role in quality control will usually be *how* something is done. And given that it's you who'll be living in the place, you have every right to be fussy. For more on quality control, see page 175.

Anyone building for themselves has to have a dream in order to get started and keep going. If those of us who do it weren't dreamers we'd go out and buy a mass-produced, ready-made home like everyone else.

Building in a falling property market

The last big downturn in the property market, in the early 1990s, saw self-builders, extenders and renovators doing well. The current crunch could provide even better opportunities

Most of us self-build to get better value, more control over design and quality, and to buy ourselves a lifestyle or location we wouldn't otherwise be able to afford. All of this still applies during the credit crunch....and can, paradoxically, play into our hands even more when times are tough.

It's no secret that mass-market house-builders have fallen on very hard times and that, at a time when Governments want more affordable housing, house-building companies have virtually shut up shop and are having difficulty selling even the stock they already have.

The cost of building land is falling, though, as large-scale operators need to maintain cash flow and have to sell off sites, both large and small. Add to this the small-to-medium builders and speculators who are holding land, and it's easy to see that the main thing that drives house prices – land - is going to fall yet further in price.

The thing is that, crunch or no crunch, the actual cost of building a house doesn't change all that much once you strip out the land cost, so as land gets cheaper and more available, self-builders can do very well.

Of course, self-builders aren't a homogenous group. Some of us will lose our jobs, others fall foul of ill health or divorce, and so on. Averse life events can kill off even the best-laid plans, and of course, most of us will have a business or a job to run, or other financial commitments that could cause us grief, whatever our self-build intentions. All this makes it impossible to generalise about how the crunch will affect self-builders. Some will die a financial death and others will thrive.

This said, all being equal, the credit crunch can provide wonderful opportunities, if we're brave enough to take them.

As always, the smaller the debt you're holding, the better position you'll be in. In general, self-builders don't borrow as large a proportion of their home's value as do other home-owners. This is partly because some start out with a chunk of capital from selling their existing home; others cut their coat according to their cloth when budgeting in the first place; but mostly, the day we complete our self-build we enjoy between a 20 and 30% uplift in value. This gives us some very welcome financial 'fat' even before we move in. And lenders love this.

On the other side of the coin, though, many self-builders over recent years have used the rising value of land as a buffer against sloppy financial planning and cost control. Many who went, even quite dramatically, over budget – kidding themselves they were successful 'developers' – saved their financial skins only because the property market in general was rising so fast it bailed them out.

This sort of sloppy planning will now have to end, and we'll all need to look more carefully at budgeting and specifying, right from Day One. This is a time for reality-testing and controlling expectations at every stage.

Getting the money together

Although the mainstream mortgage market is nothing short of terrible at the moment, this isn't the case for self-build mortgages. It's still possible to get 90% mortgages from specialist sources. This is largely because lenders see self-builders as a safe bet, and because they know they build larger, better-quality homes that will be easier to get rid of if they have to repossess them. Lenders are also only too aware that because they are risking only the amount that they have lent on work completed (though there are mortgage companies that will lend for work ahead of its completion), they're not at that great a risk at any time.

This said, lenders are becoming stricter about who they lend to, even in the self-build market. You may find yourself jumping through a few more hoops, and having to satisfy your lender you're a good bet but even doing this you'll still be way ahead of your neighbours looking for a normal mortgage. There are nearly 40 lending institutions in the ROI and UK who'll want your business, even in the credit crunch, so shop around. Another factor in favour of self-builders is that they are, on average, older (aged between 40 and 50) and more financially stable than the average person seeking a mortgage.

Self-builders usually try to stay in their own home while completing their new one but I'd strongly advise against this now. Get your own home sold and then rent, preferably in the area where your new home will be, so your children can start at their schools and you can become part of the local community. Carrying two debts in a credit crunch isn't courageous....it's mad. This could mean selling your existing home for less than you'd hoped, so be careful with your budgeting for the new place. Assume the worst, and you won't go far wrong. After all, there's no point lusting after that wonderful plot that seems such a bargain if you have to take such a hit on your own home that your new-build is blown out of the water.

Plots galore

As every prospective self-builder knows only too well, the number one challenge has always been finding that great plot. The credit crunch is the best thing that has happened in this context. All kinds of land owners, investors and holders are looking to get some cash in their pockets. Even some people with a large garden who'd never have thought of selling it could be trying to keep their financial heads above water and will sell. All such people with financial problems present a great opportunity for the self-builder. As always, the secret is to find that motivated seller.

We'll all need to look more carefully at budgeting and specifying, right from Day One

PlotSearch, BuildStore's land-finding database, has noted two major trends over the last twelve months. First, the number of plots for sale is 50% more than at the same time in early 2008, and second, fewer plots are being sold. This means more are actually available for self-builders. And some can be bought at bargain prices. There are also great bargains to be had at auctions, both for land and renovation projects. Plotfinder.net is another good source of sites, and there are many others.

If you're starting your self-build now you'll probably take about two years to complete it, by which time the property market could be starting to look up a little. In other words, taking your time, once you've bought your land, could be in your favour. This said, be very careful indeed when buying land at the moment, as desperate sellers are trying things on in order to secure a speedy sale. Take the best legal advice, as making a mistake now could cost you dearly. If something appears too good to be true....it probably is!

Available builders

As the recession hits builders of all sizes, there are lots of highly-skilled tradesmen around looking for work. On a project I was involved in recently we secured a really good builder who'd normally have work pre-booked for at least a year, happy to start the following week, after a cancellation. This is a very common story.

Try to be as robust as you can in not paying for materials or work in advance

A real problem now, though, is whether or not your chosen builder will still be in business by the end of your project. Builders traditionally expose themselves to financial risk by funding each stage up-front, only to be paid when a particular part of the work is complete. I am increasingly finding that builders and even suppliers simply won't do this, even if I know them well and have traded with them for years. They are so concerned about never getting paid that they are demanding cash up front. This tricky situation works both ways, of course, as it can be virtually impossible to discover whether your chosen builder or supplier is in financial trouble. He may be a very old-established trader and still go bust if his customers won't, or can't, pay him. All I can advise is to try to be as robust as you can in not paying for materials or work in advance. But you might not be able to achieve much.

When it comes to individual trades: OK, thousands of European tradesmen have gone back to their home countries, for many reasons, but there are still lots of good people around. The large house-builders have also let thousands of tradesmen go, so they too are available for work. Some people fear their mind-set won't be suited to the small, self-build site but this hasn't been my experience. In fact, they often bring helpful skills, experience and insights from working on a larger scale.

What you probably won't find is tradesmen willing to work for less money. Good, well-qualified people are still busy, credit crunch or not, and even middle-quality trades are still charging what they used to. As 2009 progresses, this situation may change.

Building materials

It should be possible, in an economic downturn, to obtain building materials at bargain prices. But this hasn't been my experience. OK, you'll be able to get bargain kitchens, furniture, bathrooms, flooring and certain other supplies you'll need but actual basic 'heavyside' building material prices don't seem to be responding to the current financial difficulties. I suspect that as the recession deepens, merchants will have to reduce prices to stay in business.

Selling your self-build

Although the overwhelming majority of self-builders are creating a home for themselves to live in rather than looking to make a short-term profit (one of the reasons institutions like to lend them money), in the current financial climate anything can happen to make it vital to sell up even, perhaps, before your build is complete.

Of course this is heart-breaking at a personal level, especially if you've already invested a lot of yourself in the project. But try to put a positive spin on it.

You'll have a better-than-average-quality property to sell, and probably one that is larger than average. And on a nicer plot. There's still a relative shortage of such properties and thus a demand for them. More than 60% of new builds in general are small flats and less than are quarter detached homes. So you're in with a better chance of a sale right from the start. Also, you'll be able to incorporate features and finishes that your buyer would like to have, if they buy early enough in the build cycle. This obviously means biting on the bullet early enough to be able to make this happen. If you put off the day you sell you'll have a less marketable house, which will be bad news in difficult times.

All this means advertising your home, perhaps through an agent that specialises in selling new homes, earlier than you'd think. Once you have a committed buyer on board you'll get their deposit and, hopefully, be able to complete the build. If this doesn't look like being the case, don't go this route or you could end up in serious legal trouble – having taken their money but being unable to complete the house for them. If in any doubt, sell the place as is, and let them complete it. With a contract in hand, though, you might be able to get a bridging loan from your lender but these loans are hard to come by at the moment and will cost a lot to service. This said, this could still be the best way to go if your profit from the sale will allow it.

Of course, you could save money by selling the place yourself through websites and other media.

The sale of an unfinished property like this will call for careful legal and commercial footwork because, very obviously, you won't get the whole sale price until the place is totally finished and the contract is not only exchanged but completed. The gap between these two parts of the legal selling process could be a year or more. This long timescale could also make it hard to price your property as either party could lose out in the current fluctuating market. This is a commercial decision you'll have to make, though, if you are going this route.

I maintain that the future is set fair

Self-building into the future

I know that only about 20,000 people self-build each year in the UK and ROI combined and that's it's only a small proportion of all new-builds but I maintain that the future is set fair. As plots become more available at reasonable prices and builders and tradesmen happy to work for affordable profits and wages, the segment of the property market that this sector of the building scene contributes to might just become really significant.

Self-building has always been seen as somewhat of a 'consenting adults', minority pastime. But the very real contribution it could make to the housing scene should now be recognised for what it is. Hopefully, the credit crunch will hasten this process.

3 Listening – the secret of good management

Most of us think we know what we mean when we say we 'listen' to someone – it is about 'hearing' what they say. And of course it is. But there's much more to making people feeling truly heard and understood than simply acknowledging that they have spoken. All this is important right from the first day you start even to discuss your ideas with your family because you'll need to be able to listen effectively to everyone involved, including yourself. If you don't, your project could get off to a terrible start and you'll lose the support of important family members, or even your partner.

Because of all this I'm starting off your journey to becoming a good project manager by looking at the business of listening to people.

Verbal communication is a highly complex affair. When I say to my plumber, 'I'd like the bath in the corner', he'll think he's understood what the words 'bath' and 'corner' mean and will work accordingly. But what I may actually have meant by these words could have been entirely different. At the very simplest level, there are four corners to the room and many baths in the showroom. 'I didn't mean *that* bath in *that* corner!'

Every time we try to communicate something to another person, the thing we intend to say is already somewhat modified and 'filtered' by our own unconscious before it even comes out of our mouth. We then say it (which may not even really be exactly what we meant deep down) and this is 'heard' by our listener.

His or her unconscious now kicks in and they hear what they think they have perceived. This could now be altered yet again by their unconscious before they respond or act.

Clearly, then, there are several stages during which misunderstandings and mis-expressions can occur, giving rise to subsequent confusion.

On matters to do with your building project, all of this comes into play in spades. You'll often be communicating at the edges of your knowledge and competence, and you'll be surrounded by people making assumptions. Of course, you yourself will also be making assumptions.

But, as the Americans say, to assume is to make an ASS out of U and ME! The path to building hell is paved with well-intentioned assumptions. And this applies from adding a garage to your home right up to a major contractor building a shopping centre.

So how to get around this? One answer is obviously not to make assumptions. Another is to seek clarification whenever possible. But more important still is to be sure you are listening empathically to all those around you.

And here I'm making a very basic assertion – that all verbal communication involves an emotional exchange, whether we like it or not. And when we are building our own home, emotions run high, whether or not they are openly expressed. Everyone we deal with also has their personal emotional agenda, however professional they are. Clearly something different is needed. This something is empathic listening. So how do you do it?

What is empathic listening?

First off, empathy is not sympathy. Whenever I teach empathy to couples or groups I find people say in exercises, 'I know exactly how you feel.' This is usually followed closely by the recounting of some sort of incident that has happened to them that illustrates how well placed they are to understand what the other person is saying or feeling. This sort of sympathetic approach, in which the listener mirrors what the other is saying, can be useful later but not until they get good at being empathic.

The trouble with being sympathetic is that however much you think you're helping the other person, the very fact that you are talking about yourself takes the spotlight off them and suddenly you find you're doing your stuff, not theirs. Many people hijack almost all conversations in this way and, as a result, those around them say they never feel heard.

Empathy is very different in that when I am being empathic with you I put my own business to one side and imagine standing in your shoes. By doing this I can, if only for a few moments, feel with you what you are feeling. I cannot, of course, feel your feelings for you – and I don't want to, they are yours, not mine – but I can identify with you very deeply.

This said, there are no prizes for being a clever clogs, simply to be able to say, 'I really know what Jane is feeling'. You have to act on this information in a way that helps the situation. The secret of good empathic listening is to respond in a way that makes the speaker feel understood.

Listening empathically usually helps

To get things moving, ask yourself:

- How do you confuse sympathy with empathy in daily life?
- How many feelings words can you name?
- What sorts of feelings do you find it hard/easy to identify?
- When people are listening to you, what makes you feel most understood?

Your action plan

There are three main steps to empathic listening:

First, put your own business to one side. Listen solely to what the speaker is saying. This can be terribly hard to do in our ego-based culture. Men, especially, find this hard to do, and especially so in the presence of other men (as on a building site). With practice, though, you'll be able to change the way you behave in only a few weeks.

Unfortunately, many of us have considerable 'roadblocks' to doing this. See which of the following apply to you:

Common roadblocks include:

- I am preoccupied
- My feelings about what is being said are too strong
- My arrogance makes others feel their thoughts are worthless
- I automatically find fault/criticise/evaluate
- I interrupt all the time
- I get defensive
- I jump to premature conclusions

And so on. There are many more.

The second part of empathic listening is to identify the main emotion of the person you're listening to. Sometimes this is really easy. If your electrician is fuming because you haven't got the delivery he's been waiting for, it is pretty obvious. But many emotions are much less clear than this. Yet they still need identifying.

It can be hard for many people even to name a few common emotions. Here are some examples:

- sadness
- disappointment
- doubt
- inadequacy
- shock
- disgust
- irritability
- fury
- rage
- surprise
- boredom
- excitement
- despair
- relief
- excitement

....and there are many more.

When trying to identify the other person's main emotion, take into account their body language as well as what they are saying. This can often be a give-away. As you get really good at it you'll be able to spot cross-communication – in which the person says one thing but their body language says another.

It's also helpful, as you get better at all this, to try to identify any *underlying* emotions. Your builder is angry that you've changed your mind for the third time on where you want the cooker to go, but what else is going on? Is he actually upset because he's a stickler for schedules and these delays have put him back for his next job...where he'll come across as unreliable? His underlying feeling here could be fear...that he'll lose his next contract. So your task is not only to identify his anger but also to 'hear' empathically his underlying fear.

The third and final stage of empathic listening is feeding back the emotions you have identified. This at first sounds really corny but in fact it is the most vital part of the process. If,

When trying to identify the other person's main emotion, take into account their body language as well as what they are saying

in the example above, you can say, 'It seems to me you're really upset about me changing my mind about where to put the cooker...And I expect it's a damn nuisance because it'll put you late with your next job and I know you like to start when you say you will.'

However cross your builder was at the start, he now cannot go on being too upset because you have acknowledged that he is angry, and better yet, you have made a kind and insightful comment to him that shows you value him. Few people in this situation go on being angry. In one short sentence you have defused what could have been a difficult situation or, worse, one that could have led him to pull his men off the site. Note that I have not said you are to apologise for changing your mind. This is *your* stuff. In this interchange you have concentrated solely on *his* emotions. You have not said how hard it is for you to make decisions about where to put the cooker. You have listened to him entirely.

You'll notice in the response above I have used the phrase, 'It seems to me...' This is a terrific phrase. It really starts to get things moving. When discussing window choices with your architect, for example, you might at some stage say, 'It seems to me you're keen that I go for tilt-and-turn windows'. If this is indeed the case, he can say so and can clarify accordingly. If it is not true, and it's your perception that you are being pushed into a choice you're not happy with, the matter can be easily sorted out. Again, in one simple sentence you can clear up something that could otherwise have taken minutes, hours, or even weeks!

Listening to professionals

During your project you'll be listening a lot to the opinions, feelings, judgements, self-serving nonsense, variations of the truth, hollow apologies, and the assumptions of all manner of professionals. Right from the day you walk into an estate agent to choose your property or site you'll be learning how to listen with a very particular and unique hat on. After all, you're not buying the place like someone else would. Your agenda could be that the garden looks big enough to slip in another house. How you now listen to the estate agent will change accordingly. What is left unsaid (by both parties) can often be more instructive than what is actually said. The skill is 'hearing' the unsaid.

During your project you'll be listening a lot to the opinions, feelings, judgements, self–serving nonsense, variations of the truth, hollow apologies, and the assumptions of all manner of professionals

In case you think what I've just said makes you appear too much like a 'developer' when you'd imagined you were simply trying to build a home for your family, think again. The moment you embark on your building project you will, in reality, become a developer, if only for this one build. Where people go wrong time and again is trying to achieve a professional outcome whilst acting like an amateur. OK, early on you'll be a novice developer but the sooner you start thinking like a professional one, the better result you'll get. My aim in this whole book is to help you to become more professional. And there are few areas where this will be more vital than when dealing with the full-time professionals.

All professionals have both a personal and a 'group' way of behaving and communicating. Professionals everywhere – be they brain surgeons or town planners – belong to 'trade clubs'. Within these there are, of course, huge individual and personality variations. In general, though, estate agents, planners, architects, plumbers, and so on have their own 'languages'. Some of this 'club' jargon serves to obscure true communication. Being good at what you are trying to achieve means hearing each of these languages in their own particular way and translating what you hear to your personal advantage.

When dealing with anything to do with property and building, if something appears too good to be true, it usually is!

Much of this comes with experience, of course, but the consistent rules of listening to factual presentations remain. The critical thing, in my view, is to clarify, as they say in legal documents...'For the avoidance of doubt.' Then, when you think you understand something, clarify it again. When dealing with anything to do with property and building, if something appears too good to be true, it usually is! It takes experience and a few bloodied noses to get to the stage where you can hear what is not being said; can separate bullshit from reality; can see when you are being hoodwinked or frankly lied to; and so on. Remember that all the professionals with whom you'll deal will be doing their thing every day of the week and will have learned to cover every possible base over years of practice. Although this is a steep learning curve it can also be a great achievement as you learn the ropes.

Listening to yourself

Unless you're some sort of masochist, you'll want your build to be as pleasurable as possible. This will mean learning how to listen to yourself, and by doing so to love and look after yourself.

Right from the start it's vital to understand what work you can realistically do yourself. What tasks should you subcontract? How much pressure can you reasonably live with given you have a full-time job? How will everything affect your family? Will you have to live away from them on the site while you build? How will all this affect you?

It can be helpful to talk all this through with someone who really cares about you. This may not be your partner...who may have other agendas – like they want a brilliant house they otherwise couldn't afford and they want it now!

Above all, listen to your inner voice. Don't get carried away on the basis that because something can be done, it should be done. Try to be insightful about why you are doing it at all. Try to balance all the plusses and minuses on this. Be as realistic as you can be. If you're inexperienced, listen to what others say about what is actually and realistically possible. You are not Superman and don't have to drive yourself to a nervous breakdown to prove you are. Be gentle on yourself...and those around you. If your health isn't great; if your relationship is rocky; if your kids are troublesome; if you have dependent parents who call on your time; or if things are hell at work – think again before you even start.

Once you have completed your build, listen to yourself again. Take pride in your achievement. Indulge yourself by enjoying living in it. Try not to go round all the time finding faults. Did you enjoy the process? Would you do it again? Will you do it again? What do the family say about all this?

When listening to yourself at the end of the project I predict you'll acknowledge that you have undergone a considerable transformation in ways you could never have expected. Take pleasure in these newfound skills...no one can take them away from you. Delight in them and see how they can enrich your life and that of those around you off the building site.

4 Getting started

When we set out to build ourselves a home or to do any major building work, the last thing we want is to become an accountant! Yet, reality being what it is, keeping a watchful eye on the finances can make that vital difference between having a good experience and ending up with a nightmare. Almost all self-builds over-run their budget....some disastrously so. For most of us, the starting point is deciding how much cash we can lay our hands on. This can be even more important than knowing, in any detail, what we intend to build. Many self-builders go about this the wrong way. They start to 'live' in their proposed house in their mind, fall in love with the idea and then try to make it work financially. Unfortunately, dreams are free but building work isn't.

Deciding what you want and what you need

Start off by deciding what it is you really need, rather than want, from your new build. Make a list of priorities you absolutely must have and then add on the 'nice-to-have' elements. Bounce this around the family so all your stakeholders feel involved. It's now you'll need to start managing everyone's expectations. And this is vital because until you do this you won't even know where to start on your financial planning. I look at how to decide on wants and needs in more detail on page 116.

Next, sit down with your partner or other family financial stakeholders (such as Granny, who may be lending you some cash) and work out your personal finances. How much money do you actually have? How much can you borrow against your income? Will another family member be contributing in some way? What are your savings like? If you're building a new home what, realistically, will you get for your existing place on selling up?

Some solid homework should follow this conversation:

- Get your current house valued by three estate agents. Try to ascertain how long it will take to sell. You may not sell for some time so try to find out how the property market is moving in your area
- Start finding out about lending institutions
- Meet with your bank manager and let him know what you're up to
- Talk to your accountant (or IFA...independent financial adviser), if you have one. If you don't, this could be a good time to appoint one
- Make a realistic (preferably pessimistic) assessment of what your savings and investments could be worth in the future

At this early stage we tend to fool ourselves we'll have more cash available than in fact is the case. It is here that money trouble starts.

Be brutally honest with all the sums you come up with and, if anything, underestimate your income and borrowing power.

At this stage all you'll have decided is: you'd like to do the project; approximately how much money you'll have available; and that you want to take things further.

Deciding what to do

Once you've worked out how much cash you'll have, it's time to see what's possible in terms of actual building. After all, you'll be able to build only as much as you can pay for! There's absolutely no point starting out with an idea for a dream house you won't be able to build. I've seen too many couples come to grief by going this route.

> **There's absolutely no point starting out with an idea for a dream house you won't be able to build**

In my opinion, the next stage is to see an architect, or some other sort of professional designer. He doesn't have to be the one you'll eventually work with (see page 42) but should be well worth a small outlay at this stage. Talk through your wish list and start to get a handle on what this proposed project will actually cost to build. If you choose someone local to the site of a new-build he'll know the likely cost of a plot of land, what local builders charge per square metre to build and will also be able to guide you on his, and other professional, costs. From now on, whenever I refer to your new build as if it were a whole new house, I'm also talking about a renovation, extension, or any major new building work.

This consultation is often a wake-up call for would-be self-builders. And it should be. For a very modest amount of money, it's a great start. When I conduct this sort of consultation with people at this stage of their build, I find they usually have absolutely no idea what the whole project will cost. And why should they? I couldn't begin to guess how much it would cost to replace the engine in my car.

Now is the time to get real about what you're likely to be able to afford. OK, you'd wanted a detached, four-bed place on two acres, with a huge double garage and a self-contained annex for Granny but it turns out you'll have to settle for three beds on an eighth of an acre, a bed-sit for Granny and no garage.

> **Whenever I refer to your new build as if it were a whole new house, I'm also talking about a renovation, extension, or any major new building work**

Knowing this, it's time for a re-think. Do you still want to proceed? More couples should back out at this stage than actually do. I know this takes courage, but it's much too dangerous for your finances, your family and your relationships to plough on with a plan that is financially doomed from the start.

Getting the money

But even once you've made this first and vital decision – that you'd like to take things further – there's no cash in the kitty until you make it happen. Wishful thinking will get you nowhere. The most important next step is thus to start assessing costs and how you'll be able to get the money together.

There are nearly forty institutions in the UK and Northern Ireland that will be interested in your business as a self-builder of a new home, most of whom will lend up to 75% of the build cost. Some will lend towards the land, and others won't, or will demand a huge deposit on the land purchase. Look in the self-build magazines where these people advertise; surf the web; talk to your bank manager and perhaps to the architect you've already met. Between all these sources you'll come up with a few good starting points. Who will lend you what will depend on your earnings and other security you can offer. If you are self-employed, have little or no cash of your own to put down, or are looking to do the build as a sell-on, then expect many more problems raising the finance. Any lender will also want to see that you've thought everything through and have a credible presentation.

Sources of money

There are lots of ways of getting cash for your build. Some methods will best suit renovations and extensions to your existing home, others (see also above) are better for new-builds. In reality, working with an independent financial advisor who knows your affairs, you'll be able to cobble together a package from several sources. Many self-builders use a combination of: their own savings, borrowings from a relative, equity from a previous home, and borrowed cash from an institution.

Let's look at each in turn:

Use your own money

Pros:

- You've already got it and won't need to involve outsiders
- It's quicker and simpler than anything else...especially when institutions are being cautious
- You'll work harder to bring your project in on budget knowing your pot of money is fixed...spending your own money refines the mind!

Cons:

- Having to go through outsiders can make you more critical and cautious as you'll need to convince them about everything
- You might be able to use your money better by doing something else (perhaps investing it elsewhere) and borrowing more cheaply from an institution
- You could find yourself in difficulty when you run out of cash

Borrow from relatives

Pros:

- OK for small amounts but dangerous for large ones (unless they're very rich!)
- Likely to be flexible about repayments (check this at the start)
- Some of the loan could be transformed into a gift at some stage, especially if Inheritance Tax is involved (talk to your IFA)

Cons:

- Difficult mixing business with family
- They may not have more funds available when you run over budget
- Other family members may take an adverse view
- Could become problematic if donor family member's financial circumstances change

Home improvement grants

Pros:

- Free

Cons:

- Hard to get, even for Listed Buildings. Talk to your council or go to www.english-heritage.org.uk

Increase your existing mortgage

Pros:

- You already have a track record with your lender
- They'll be happy to lend (within reason) if you're improving a house in which they already have a financial interest
- They know the value of your place and have security in it already
- You can spread new borrowings over the remaining duration of your existing loan

Cons:

- It'll take time to organise
- It could be expensive (because of penalties) to pay back lumps of cash if you want to in the future
- Interest rates could rise over the years, making things more expensive than you'd planned
- You'll have to pay to have your place valued
- They'll want some sort of administration charge, (which could run into hundreds of pounds)
- Your lender will have a ceiling on the minimum amount of equity they'll want you to retain (somewhere between five and fifteen per cent)
- You may have to pay a mortgage indemnity premium (which can cost thousands)

Switch your mortgage

Pros:

- It could be time to take stock of your mortgage anyway. Are you getting the best rate? Could you change the length of pay-back to suit you better?

Cons:

- There could be penalties for paying off your current mortgage early
- Other costs are involved
- It can take a lot of time to find the best deal
- New lenders may not want to go along with your plans
- Your current lender may be your best bet, if only because they know you. You might be less attractive to new lenders than you imagine (for example, bad credit risk, CCJs, or being self-employed)

Take out a loan

Pros:

- By taking out a 'second charge' on your property a lender will be confident they'll get their cash back because they have the right to sell your home to do so. This is known as a 'secured loan'. You can, alternatively, take out an unsecured loan, usually for smaller amounts, but although this is quicker it'll cost a lot more
- Can be good if you want your total borrowings (mortgage plus loan) to be greater than the value of your home.... mortgage companies won't do this
- A good method (with a second charge) if you've had financial problems (CCJs or bad debts) or are self-employed
- Few, if any, costs (unlike with increasing your mortgage)

Cons:

- Your home is at risk
- It can be hard (or impossible) to secure other, subsequent, borrowings against your home, even if you have lots of equity
- Lenders don't like 'third charges'
- Some companies may insist on your paying 'protection insurance'...to cover all, or part, of your repayments should you be unable to honour them. Look carefully at the rates and penalties
- Usually costs more, sometimes a lot more, than a mortgage

'And to think they called me a mad enthusiast!

Supplier's financing schemes

Given that there's good profit to be made from lending people money, many suppliers in the building world offer their own finance packages. This can apply to anything from a kitchen to an entire kit house. Such schemes are usually more expensive than your doing the deal direct, as a middle man makes a profit. Some companies have their own branded financial service business; others refer you to a finance company and take a commission or an introduction fee. Either way, you pay. If you are thinking of going this route, talk to your IFA. Be aware that an eagerly-offered discount on a product can soon be eaten up by costly financing.

A sub-set of this is a buy-now-pay-later deal. Such deals are commonly offered in the kitchen trade and in certain other domestic build areas. You put down a deposit then pay in instalments over an agreed period. Payment 'holidays' may be offered and are great, provided you don't then have to pay an inflated interest rate at the end of the holiday.

Compare what this all costs with other money sources. Be wary of payment protection insurance costs and read all the small print.

When talking to potential lenders about a new-build or a substantial extension or renovation, be prepared to show them a drawing of the proposed work; details of the plot, if it's a new-build (with agent's brochure); a broad timetable of when you'll need the money (in stages over, say, one year from build start); a copy of the planning permission, if you have it; and your building cost estimate from your architect. If you can also detail the costs listed below, they'll be mega-impressed.

A helpful website on sourcing finance in troubled times is www.moneyfacts.co.uk

What things will cost

Now you've seen the money-bags and it looks as if the project is a runner in principle, for money you're likely to be able to afford, it's time to assess the real costs rather than the back-of-an-envelope guesstimates you and your architect will have generated thus far.

If you're building a new house, the most important starting point is your plot. It is easy today, given the shortage of plots with planning permission, to spend a third of your entire available budget on the site. And for a brilliant site, it can be more. But remember – you still only have your finite budget to spend. So if you go for a stunning plot, you'll have to build a smaller, or poorer-quality, house. Or both. This might still make sense if you think you'll be able to build on or improve later when you come into more cash.

Finding a plot

The secret here is to be realistic right from the start. Delicious plots are very hard to find. And when they are available, they cost a fortune or are snapped up by professionals. In a falling property market plots can be easier to find as developers and especially small builders have to off-load sites to keep afloat. But this doesn't mean you'll be flooded with great plots at bargain prices. What it usually means is that plots that would otherwise be completely unavailable, slowly become so.

It's now time to assess the real costs rather than the back-of-an-envelope guesstimates

Depending on how geographically flexible you can be it can make sense to look in more remote locations, a long way from large cities. Many would-be self-builders find it hard to accept they'll have to move away to get their dream. It's probably this that explains the huge proportion of drop-outs from the pool of 'dream builders'. More than half of the 20,000 or so self-builds completed every year in the UK are built in Wales, Scotland and Northern Ireland. Note that very few indeed are built in the expensive South-East.....and when they are, the people often already own the land (for example, their garden).

Most would-be self-builders still cherish the notion that somewhere out there is a little old lady sitting on a place they could buy for next to nothing and put a dream house in its place. I'm afraid those days are long gone. By twenty years, or more. Little old ladies have professional advisers, and financially-aware kids, all of whom ensure the vendor gets the very best price for their place. Most first-time builders are shocked at what land costs but it's a seller's market and people get what they can. When pricing such sites, estate agents work on the principle that the house, once built, will be worth X. From this they deduct the cost of construction, and reckon the site is worth the remainder. This is clearly a strategy aimed at end-users. No professional developer thinks like this because they have to make a profit. When I evaluate sites for clients I never consider such propositions because there's no 'fat' in it for my client. This is one of the many reasons professional developers and their advisors pick up properties before they ever get near the 'retail' market. Exceptions to this are really major conversions, especially

It's vital to know if there any rights of way across your land

historic ones. Here the pros often don't want to get involved because such builds tie up cash they could be churning in other, simpler, ways and because there are so many imponderables that even they cannot price or time the job accurately. These jobs are really only for the mad enthusiast.

As you can see from the list on page 27, finding your plot is a serious job of work. You'll need to persist, perhaps for as long as a year or two, to get what you want.

On balance it's probably wise to buy a plot only if it has planning permission. This could be outline or full permission. Early on in your self-building career I think it's foolish to saddle yourself with a high-risk gamble involving land with no permission.

A possible way round this is to buy an option. Here, you enter into a legal agreement with the owner that he won't sell to anyone else for, say, two or three years while you get yourself sorted out (planning permission, finances etc). Obviously this will cost you (perhaps 5% of the plot value) but in return you'll have agreed a price, which, in a rising market, could turn out to be in your favour. However, in a strongly-rising market vendors don't need to go down this route...they can find someone who'll pay what they want there and then and take the risks on the chin.

Selling an option can favour the vendor in another way if you agree between you that you'll try for the best possible density of new houses you can achieve. If successful with more units than you both originally thought, this is then subsequently reflected in a higher return to him. Some vendors will be delighted to let you do all the work for them to achieve a better result than they could be bothered with. You, in return, will get your site and even possibly the chance to build a spec house as well. This is good when times are tough.

There are many ways of finding a plot:

- Look in the Self-build magazines, where a myriad of opportunities is laid out before you
- Keep your eye on the estate agents in your target areas. Be forceful, pro-active and persistent, calling your contacts every week or two to see what's coming on. By the time it's on their website, you're too late
- Look on the internet for plot-finding websites. There are many. Some are really sophisticated
- Employ a professional plot finder. Ideally, someone in planning consultancy is best. An extension of this is to contact all manner of property-based professionals (architects, planning consultants, surveyors etc) locally. They may have a client who has a plot but for whatever reason doesn't want to, or can't, develop it themselves. At least by doing this you're fishing in the right pool, which increases your chances
- Use a website that details recent planning decisions so you can get in there quickly with an offer
- Talk to your council and local utility companies. Both have large land holdings, parcels of which they sell off from time to time
- Looking through council planning records can be fruitful. All the details of planning permissions are in the public domain. Look at what permission was granted on a site, go there and see if it's actually been built. If it hasn't, could the owners have come up against a personal barrier that has stopped them? Could you take over their planning?
- Self-build package companies often have sources of sites. OK, they'll expect you to use them for your build but this could work out well even if you hadn't given it much thought until now
- Building companies have land banks for their own future use. It's not common but they can sometimes be persuaded to sell off a plot that no longer suits them, or because short-term cash flow problems mean they need to release funds. It's worth asking
- Make it known among your friends that you're prepared to offer a reward if they find you a plot. This shows how serious you are and it could be worth the £1,000 to get what you want
- Keep your eyes and ears open locally so you'll be aware of things on the grape-vine. I know people who found their plot while drinking in a pub!
- Approach home owners who have large gardens or spare land around their homes. It's a long shot but can work. Google Earth can help you spot possible plots
- Advertise in the Wanted section of the local paper. There might just be the odd plot advertised for sale in the paper too
- Drive, or better still, walk or cycle round your proposed area. You'll be amazed what you'll see when you're not cocooned in a car. After all, you're looking for a jewel that may be hidden behind a fence or among overgrown trees and brush. This detective work can be fun and is a particularly good way of finding demolition, change-of-use and conversion opportunities
- Go to property auctions. This is more tricky, as you'll be up against the pros, who can build much more cheaply than you (they have salaried workmen who need continuity of employment) and still turn a profit. Problems here include the fact that you'll be expected to put down a ten per cent deposit at the auction. This means you'll have to have done your homework on the site, and this can cost a lot of money.....all to be wasted if you don't secure the purchase

Whatever you think you want to buy, though, don't move a muscle without taking legal advice. It's easy for even seasoned professionals to get it wrong, so beware. Your solicitor can ensure that the planning permission the sellers claim to have is what it says it is. There are many wrinkles here. For example, there may be planning permission but only for an already-agreed-upon design. And you might not want it. Without a doubt some designs can be changed but it can take ages and is a big gamble. There may also be planning but only on a part of the site that won't suit you. And so on.

Your lawyer will also look into the following:

Is there a ransom strip? I've had three sites over the years blighted by these. Everything seems great until you discover that part of the land (often essential for access or some vital service) is either owned by someone else or by the same party, who wants blood from you. Buying out such a strip can be hugely expensive. They have you over a barrel.

Rights of way and wayleaves. Rights of way are often very ancient in the UK and can be hard or impossible to change. If you are happy having ramblers striding through your garden, fine, but remember it'll reduce your value when you come to sell. A wayleave is a legal arrangement where other peoples' services or even access road crosses your land. Again, you might be relaxed about this but many people won't contemplate buying a house with a shared drive, for example....and it could mean higher insurances and more difficult financing.

Boundaries are a perpetual nightmare. I work a lot in the Republic of Ireland where the delineation of rural land ownership isn't what it is in the UK. This can be a pain. But even in the highly-regulated UK, things can be complicated enough as vast numbers of properties and land-holdings aren't registered as they should be. Although it's by no means like in Spain, the seller may not actually own what he claims (possibly in good faith). I had a serious boundary problem on one project. The whole build depended on the disputed land for its viability. The Land Registry is supposed to hold a record of who owns every piece of land but in practice this isn't the case. It wasn't on mine. Only careful work by your lawyer will satisfy you on this. If you can't be satisfied, walk away.

Covenants are another difficult area. Many properties, but especially building plots, are sold with conditions (placed by the vendor, or even a previous owner) that govern what can be built on them. The giant supermarkets do this all the time. They'll put a site on the market but impose such restrictive covenants that rivals cannot use it to create a new (competing) store. Things are usually more benign in the residential market but they can still ruin your plans. Such covenants might restrict: what you can build; how many houses you can build (dream on if you thought you'd get another house in there to sell at a huge profit!); what sort of boundaries you'll have to erect; what trees and other screening they want left; and so on. Some of these apparently simple things can cost a mint, so beware.

Lots of people are drawn to the idea of renovating a building that never was a domestic dwelling

So far I've assumed you're looking for a naked plot....a green field site. But you might not be. An alternative is to go for an existing building in a desirable location and then see what can be done. It could either be removed or massively altered to create the home you want. Lots of people are drawn to the idea of renovating a building that never was a domestic dwelling. I've done two such projects – one an old grain store with a floor area of more than 12,000 square feet. The delight of turning a dilapidated building into a beautiful home cannot be equalled and for those of us with a 'green' agenda, this recycling is a further plus.

Given there's a place there already the planners are usually more lenient compared with building in a farmer's field! But apart from the fact that there may already be some services in place, if you're lucky, the good news often ends there. Your first difficult decision (with the help of your professionals) will be whether to knock down what's there (if the planners will let you....I've done two projects where they would not, forcing me to work with the existing) or whether you'll be better off making the most of what already exists. Even seriously experienced pros can find this a hard one to call.

Your next decision is whether you really want to renovate the place rather than knock it and start again, whatever anyone else advises. Those who are experienced with renovations, especially if the original was not residential, will confirm it's a very expensive route to go. If you want value for money, knock it down and replace it with a new-build. Anything else lands you in the world of imponderables and for this you'll need very deep pockets and a huge contingency fund. I wish I'd known this many years ago when I first started.

The thing is that, with the best will in the world, designers and architects tend to get off on this sort of project and can be insufficiently realistic about costs. A high-level conversion can cost fifty to one hundred per cent more than that of a comparable new build, so unless this is what you want, and are prepared to pay for it, be very wary indeed. A factor to bear in mind is that in a new-build you'll have to incorporate renewable energy solutions. In a conversion you won't. Do your sums very carefully when comparing the two options. The period restoration world is a sub-set of all this and is exceptionally expensive as all parties concerned imagine you have a private gold mine and so price everything accordingly!

OK, you've found your site: now to get down to some financial reality. At this point I should say that because you've found a good candidate, don't be too disappointed if all your hard work (see below) appears to come to nothing because you have to abandon the first thing you fall in love with. This is par for the course. But none of the work I now detail will be wasted. You'll be wiser and far better informed and will be able to apply your personalised financial formula to the next candidate property. This will make you more professional in your approach to the whole thing and thus better equipped to jump quickly (like the developer you are becoming) and not lose a good opportunity. Without a doubt you'll be kissing a lot of frogs before alighting on a prince.

How much to pay

Trying to assess how much to pay for your dream plot can be hard. Good sites are traded just like other valuable commodities, with people buying them never intending to build anything on them. Some such purchasers buy a site to obtain the very best planning they can, then sell it on. If you're a rookie developer be very wary and take advice. There are many landowners out there who are just waiting for a desperate first-timer to offer them a huge sum for a small piece of land, especially one with planning.

The way most property is valued is by the notion of 'comparables'. Estate agents and surveyors keep an extremely close eye on their local market and can foretell what anything will sell for with some accuracy. The problem with this method is that, whilst it works well for a terraced house in Railway Cuttings, it can be much less helpful when the commodity for sale has few, or even no, comparables. This can be the case with some plots and other properties suitable for the self-builder. A website that could be of help on this is www.buildstore.co.uk

Never worry about losing an opportunity...they're like London buses. There's always another one round the corner

The second way plots are valued is by their development potential. You may be thinking of the proposed site as a nice place for your new home but the pros will be putting their planning consultants to work on it to get a small block of flats or a nursing home!

In the end you'll have to decide what you think the site is worth to you. I know self-builders who've out-bid local developers to get what they want. And who's to say they are wrong?

But if, whatever you try, things go pear-shaped and you have to start over again on a new search, don't despair. There's an old saying in property development. 'Never worry about losing an opportunity...they're like London buses. There's always another one round the corner.' Only amateur developers disbelieve this.

The next stage after finding your plot and seeing whether you can afford it in the whole scheme of your build is to asses it for viability.

Assessing a plot

Legal obstacles. I've looked at some of these above. If the project falls at this hurdle, the rest hardly matters.

Size. There's no limit to this except, perhaps, your budget. Obviously the plot will have to be large enough to take your planned house, but even this isn't so simple. Most self-builders look for something around 1,000 metres squared (a quarter of an acre) but many settle for less. A limiting factor will be what the planners will allow you to build. If they insist on it looking like everything else in the street, you'll know right from the start what's possible size-wise. If they're prepared to be flexible on things such as footprint, design, or even a basement, you'll get your floor area on a smaller plot.

Talk to your council about their minimum requirements for space around the house for your desired plot. This varies from authority to authority.

Walk the site on a good day, armed with your camera and a long tape

Boundaries. Walk the site on a good day, armed with your camera and a long tape. It helps to have an assistant. Measure everything to see if it matches the sale details. If things don't tally, you may have to get all the interested parties together to sort things out on the site. This cannot be done in an office. Take photos of every elevation of the land and of anything that concerns you. Using a compass, discover the orientation of the land. Where does South lie?

Positioning of the house. Look very carefully where you think you want your house to go. If there's an existing building line you won't have a lot of choice. If there's already a planning or even outline permission, see what's been agreed thus far. Could you live with this? How much trouble are you prepared to go to to change it? See if you could position the house to get good south light on the back of it....and thus have a south-facing garden. How much does it matter to you, if you can't achieve this?

Expensive problems to be aware of. Look out for old buildings and structures that need demolishing. This can be expensive. Is there evidence of subsidence cracks in adjoining structures? Are there ponds, disused wells, ditches or other watery areas that look like trouble? Seek advice.

Is the area heavily treed? This might look great but how many trees are likely to have tree preservation orders that mean you won't be able to take them down? Even if you *can* remove them, a large tree lost is still trouble. The ground from where it came is de-stabilised by its removal (it had become used to the tree sucking water from it) and now starts to behave differently. This can mean a more complex foundation design. And 'more complex' always means more cash.

Is there evidence of dumping, piles of rubbish, existing concrete roads or other waste that'll have to be removed? Unless it's a naked field, look around for manholes and for signs of water and electricity supplies. These can be hard to find but, if there, could save a lot later. Or they might spell trouble.

What crosses your site? The nightmare scenario is pylons. I walk away at this point but there are those who take a view on this. Look out for signs of worn paths or other public access. Take photos and ask your solicitor to check these out. Any cables or manholes near the boundaries might mean your neighbours have services going under your place. As I write this a current project will involve us re-siting a complete sewage system after finding that our client's land had been illicitly used by the neighbours over many years to house their sewerage treatment plant along with its percolation area. Although our client won't have to pay for the remedial work, as the neighbours concede the land is not theirs, it'll hold things up while it's all sorted. And time is money.

Very obviously, you can't build over your neighbours' services...in fact there may even be a dead-zone around them that has to be avoided. On a small site this can wreck the positioning of your house completely. Diverting services is always a possibility but comes at a price.

Slopes and gradients. The best site from a building point of view is a level one. Although sloping plots are often nice to live on (provided the slope isn't too steep) because you get pleasant views, every five degrees adds considerably to your cost. One expert reckons each five degrees of slope adds about £10,000 to the cost of the build.

Once you get into heroic slopes, the price can rise exponentially as the whole build takes on a different colour entirely. I was approached recently about the potential of a site which sloped at more than 40 degrees. This took us into Los Angelean construction methods, with huge (expensive) piling to support a series of reinforced concrete floor slabs off which we could build. It also meant having a lift and creating as lightweight a structure as possible to avoid massive (masonry-based) ground loadings. This, in turn, led to a design based around steel and glass with timber-frame infills where necessary. A very expensive build indeed....and a virtually useless 'garden'!

A flat, level site is easier to build on

To make life easy, what you want is a flat site on which you can simply dig your foundations without steps in them and sit a house on them. Anything else will mean employing a structural engineer and costs will mount.

Access. The ideal site, especially for a beginner, is one that has direct, un-shared access close to a public highway. Photograph any evidence that makes you suspect others have car access from the road over your land. Even an innocuous-looking strip of land alongside the road might belong to the council – its ownership and use will need to be clarified by your solicitor.

Take photos of anything and everything that causes you concern

From the council highways department's point of view, the most important thing is that when you stand where your drive meets the road, the visibility for and of vehicles on the public roadway must be good. Obstacles such as fences, trees and even poles can make for poor sightlines and thus danger. Every council has regulations that govern the amount of view needed for any given traffic speed. If necessary, you'll usually have to create a clear line of vision, which if the road is a fast one, could mean opening up a very wide 'bell mouth' so you can see and be seen by other road users. If you have lots of land this is fine but if your site has a narrow mouth, this apparently simple access issue could kill the whole project. OK, it might be possible to buy land from a neighbour to make things happen but they may know you're over a barrel and price their strip accordingly.

Shared driveways and private roads both present problems but as with so many such things, you'll have to take a view on these. There are some great houses on private roads or with shared driveways but it means you'll have to get permissions from your neighbours. And you need only one neighbour to take a stand and you're in trouble. A private, shared road caused me a problem on one job, where it meant completely resurfacing after my construction traffic of two years wrecked it. The neighbours were extremely patient and I had my men filling in potholes all the time to keep the peace but it was all aggravation....and money!

Services. These need looking for. Ideally you want them to be simple, close to the entrance to your site and not crossing other people's land. If you don't have access to a sewer this adds cost as you'll have to install your own private sewerage treatment system but worse, it can substantially influence where you can place the house as you'll need a large percolation area for your system's outflow. If there isn't enough space for this area the development could be off. If you have a tank that needs emptying from time to time you'll have to have heavy vehicle access so this can happen. This can be a problem on some sites. Another costly nasty on sewers can occur when you are perfectly happy to install your own treatment system but the planners insist you must use mains, which could be far away and much more expensive than making your own on-site arrangements.

Flood risk. This is becoming a politically hot topic. Countless thousands of homes are built on flood plains. This doesn't mean you have to repeat the error! Your council's Local Plan and the Environment Agency will tell you what the flood risks are. Look for obvious signs yourself.

The day you buy is the day you sell. So far I've concentrated on the site itself but this is only part of the story. Unless your proposed plot is in the heart of unspoiled, protected, countryside (which I doubt!) you'll have all kinds of neighbouring issues to consider. And even this isn't entirely true. I do lots of work in rural areas that appear to have no neighbours. But of course this isn't the case. Even an apparently barren area of farmland can pose later problems, if only because rural owners like things the way they are!

Take photos of anything and everything that causes you concern. Talk to the locals. They'll be your best source of gossip that could

Check while on your site:

- Who overlooks you
- How your neighbours keep their homes
- How they park their cars (camper vans, trade vans, or whatever)
- Be very wary indeed of open areas of land in a built-up area (they could later be developed – to your disadvantage)
- Look out for noisy play areas and recreation grounds
- Consider whether any factories or other industrial developments could pose a problem. Do any of them pose noise, smell, or other pollution hazards?
- Go to the place on a busy weekday, not just on a quiet weekend (which is when most of us go out site-seeing)
- Picture your house on the site and see how it'll affect your neighbours. They too will have a view on what you intend to do

otherwise be hard to obtain. I always provoke conversation by asking about other people's efforts to develop the site. Some locals clam up but I've often been amazed at what people will let out....stuff which even a solicitor won't discover! Don't forget that any given local may have objected to a previous planning but knowing that someone some day will get it, will be delighted to rubbish previous efforts in the hopes you'll do something they like.

Call local businesses about their plans if you fear they could affect you.

Having a survey

However good you think you are, and whether you're buying a field or a building to convert or renovate, it's vital to have a survey. Specialist land surveyors and certain architects and other designers can do very detailed site surveys which will be a help when deciding exactly where the house could go (taking all the other variables into account).

However, the survey I'm talking about is one done by a building surveyor, preferably one who knows the local area and planners well. This could be the best money you'll spend early on in your project. In a brisk market it's all too easy to get carried away with enthusiasm (and not a little desperation) and end up buying something you'll regret later. You may be tempted by something the pros have long ago rejected. Be very careful.

If you think you can avoid getting professional advice on your proposed purchase, just think how silly you'll feel if, when trying to raise money, your lender asks searching questions you cannot answer. A survey will give them huge confidence and show your commitment to the project. Many people get sloppy or arrogant during years of booming property prices but once the heat goes out of market everyone starts to look more carefully at what's going on. And nowhere is this more true than those from whom you'll want cash.

Although no surveyor has X-ray eyes he'll have a lot better chance than you will at 'reading the land'. For a start he'll be aware of previous problems in the area (or even possibly on your actual site) – for example with underground streams, bad clay soil, radon, contamination, planning rejections, and so on. He'll also be able to judge whether you'll need to do test borings to assess soil condition. Of all the unforeseen expenses that make a train wreck of self-build budgets, poor ground conditions come top of the list.

It's vital to have a survey

'Bad ground', as it's known in the trade, is a devil. Anything you can do to water-proof yourself against it is worth every penny. The thing is it isn't just a matter of the building control inspector coming along and saying you'll need to take your foundation dig a metre or two deeper, and the cost of this can run into thousands. It's more serious. A good surveyor or engineer will tell you, possibly after trial digs, what type of foundation design you'll need. And complex foundations can rack up the build cost by far more than a deeper, trench-filled mass of concrete. I've seen self-builders near to tears as the foundation stage of the build drives them to financial despair.

Many good builders dig trial pits as a matter of course. These need to go down three metres close to, but not too close to, the proposed foundation. A structural engineer can then decide about foundation design. Many people understandably fear that professionals like this are more concerned about their professional liability than anything else and so take the most cautious route and specify expensive foundations that will withstand anything. This can be true but it comes down to how much you can trust the individual you employ. Anyway, when dealing with foundations, it's better to be cautious because whatever else you can repair once your place is built, you're not going to change your foundations and underpinning is a nightmare.

A good surveyor will also detect the likelihood of contaminated ground or archaeological challenges. These two plot horrors make expensively-designed foundations seem a picnic.

Now that more houses are being built on brown-field land (previously used for industrial or commercial purposes) the danger of there being chemicals and other contaminants is high. At worst, you may be compelled to remove the top metre or so of soil, have it disposed of professionally into special sites and look forward to a massive bill.

But worse than both these is the hell of finding anything remotely historical on your site. A good surveyor who knows the area should be able to alert you to this, preferably before you start burning your children's inheritance! If you find remains, you will have to foot the bill for an archaeological contractor to evaluate the site. This can eat up £10,000 if you are near other historic sites, say in a city. But the worse problem is delay. Once you get into this loop the system works very very slowly. But your lender won't stop charging you interest and your builder will go onto another job, perhaps never to return. Prevention is the best cure. Along with your surveyor's local knowledge and on-site skills, check with your city or council's Historic Environment Record. On one of my sites I spent weeks collecting historical artefacts, having historical drawings done, and taking photos of everything imaginable, compiling historical logs and other records. I then had to lodge this whole archive with the

Discovering protected wildlife can really hold things up

local university's department of archaeology before the planners would let me go ahead. This was fun at one level – and from their point of view perfectly reasonable – but had obvious drawbacks in terms of time and money!

Another 'fashionable' problem that didn't exist thirty years ago is valuable, rare, and even protected wild life. If you have such creatures on your site this too will hold you up or even prevent development altogether. Even very large corporations have come unstuck on this. Again, take professional advice if in doubt.

Getting your budget together

The basic Rule of Three applies to building, as to most projects. You can only have two of: quality; speed; or low cost. It's important to keep this in mind all the time you're planning your finances. No matter how clever you think you are, you'll never get all three – a cheap build done in double-quick time to a high quality.

On balance, given that most self-builders tend to produce a better quality product than most

Your realistic budget will include:

- The plot, plus all the costs that go into finding it (including perhaps a professional finder's fee)
- Stamp duty on buying the plot
- Land registry fees
- Area search fees
- Additional reports (for example, if anyone thinks the land could be contaminated, analysis of soil samples etc)
- Legal fees
- Arrangement fee for your lender
- Designer's/architect's original fees to get to the starting blocks
- Surveyor's fees, to be sure what you are buying into on the plot purchase
- Estate agents' fees (to asses the current value of the plot and to estimate what the final house will be worth when complete). Some agents will do this for free
- Architectural fees to design the house and secure planning permission
- Other professional fees (such as a structural engineer, project manager, or interior designer, if you're using one)
- Planning fees (paid to your local authority)
- Building Control fees (for the people from the council who come out to check up on what you're doing)
- Structural warranties
- Insurances to cover everything
- Infrastructure (development) charges paid to your local authority
- Costs to connect to the mains water and electricity
- Cost of borrowing the money for both plot and build until you can live in the house
- Actual build cost (what you pay the builder) based, at this stage, on your architect's guesstimate
- Removal costs
- Re-equipping costs (you'll need at least some new furniture, curtains etc)
- Garden, grounds, driveways, parking, fencing (unless you want to live in a wilderness)...get a ballpark figure on this from your architect
- Garage (unless already factored in, which it often isn't)
- Contingency sum (say 15% of the build cost)

- PLUS all the expenses involved in selling your existing home

- PLUS all the costs of any temporary accommodation (such as a mobile home if you are going to live on the site) or rented accommodation if you're not commercial builders, my advice is to go for a high-end plot and then to build smaller than you'd like. This will usually turn out to give a better financial return in the long term. It is all too easy to put your life and soul into a great building on a second-rate (cheap) plot and then regret it.

If you know you are 'high-end' people, start to think small but beautiful

Next, it's essential to be realistic about your aspirations. If you know you are 'high-end' people, start to think small but beautiful. If you aren't that bothered about a fabulous palace but want lots of cheap space, you'll adopt a different approach to costs right from the start.

It's now time to take your plot cost and start adding on the other things you'll have to pay for. Your architect's original ball-park estimate may well have been for the build only. Now look at that real budget. Please note I'm suggesting all this way before you've gone to the expense of having anything designed!

From the list on page 35 you'll see that the actual sum you'll pay your builder gets almost lost amongst the many other outgoings, all of which add up to serious money!

And all of this supposes you don't subsequently change your mind as the build progresses. If you do, be prepared to pay plenty for 'extras' as this is how many builders make their profit.

At this early stage you might want to look at a couple of websites. www.buildthedream.co.uk is a site that enables you to estimate the actual costs of building your project, from drawings supplied to them. I look in much more detail at how to do this on page 72. Another useful site is www.selfbuildit.co.uk This will give you some starter ideas on pricing, to get your juices going.

Having done all these sums you'll be in a realistic position to decide what you can afford. Unless you are very well off this is usually far less than you originally imagined. Now is the time to discover this.

At this stage I think it's wise to go for professional help. If you choose your architect for this task, be cautious in case he's already too close to the project. I spend a lot of time with people at this point. Given that they're usually in shock at what things actually cost, it's time to see how expectations can be managed and how to save money.

Things that save money:

- Choosing a level site with easy access to services (water, drainage, electricity, roadway, gas, telephone, cable TV)
- A building that is a simple square or rectangle on plan
- A building with a smaller floor area than you'd ideally like
- A building whose external walls are without internal angles (no Ls or Ts on plan), or curves
- Avoiding things that break through the roof – even a chimney
- Simple brickwork facings to the outside walls
- Straight runs of stairs
- Keeping circulation areas (hallways, landings and corridors) to a minimum
- Avoiding eco-build methods
- Avoiding anything reclaimed
- Using simple concrete roof tiles
- Installing ordinary radiator-based heating
- Going for mass-produced kitchens and bathrooms
- Using off-the-shelf windows and doors
- Forgetting the conservatory
- Not building a garage
- Simple lighting and lighting controls
- Avoiding hardwood floors and other expensive finishes
- Avoiding lifestyle 'toys'/data cabling/ home cinemas/pools etc

Every time you buck any item on this list it'll cost you money – sometimes very large amounts of money. If you were to ignore this list entirely you could easily double your build cost. The good news, though, is that it's possible to build something very nice indeed while following this basic list. You may need to be more creative but you'll save loads and it could mean the difference between going ahead or not.

Most self-builders produce a better quality product than most mass-market, commercial builders

I hate it when people ask me to give them a ballpark building cost because it's impossible to know what they have in mind, and because everyone wants, instinctively, to take a basic sum (say £1,000 per metre squared) and assume that this is what I said the whole project will cost. As you can see from the above list, this is not the case!

The only way to work out the actual construction cost is to put drawings out to local builders for quotations. And for this, of course, you'll need these drawings completed. I'll look on page 39 at how best to get these done but first let's look at where you'll live while your build is taking place.

Deciding where to live

Unless you're doing a massive renovation or extension on your home you'll probably want, or have, to continue living in it while you build. You can also stay put if you are building in your garden.

However, when building an entire new house in another location there are lots of accommodation issues to take into account. I'm talking about them here, while thinking about money, because if your build takes 18 to 24 months, where you live could materially affect your finances. And given that most of us who opt for the self-build route are pretty stretched financially, this can become a serious issue.

There are really only three major options;

Stay living at home

Pros:

- It's what you've got and is familiar
- It involves the minimum of disruption
- It'll go down best with the family
- It's nice to go back to and leave the site behind each day
- In a booming property market the value of your home could be rising, thus contributing to your overall kitty of cash
- You may be able to create a comfortable 'project office' somewhere if you don't already have a home office
- Your partner may contribute to administrative tasks in between his or her other domestic duties

Cons:

- Once the new house becomes near-habitable you'll be funding two places at once (assuming you have borrowings on both properties)
- Not having the site under your nose makes it easier to lose touch with it and even to switch off for the odd day or two
- You won't be able to keep a watchful eye on the site's security
- You may have an added journey each day if you don't live very close to your build: this could be tiring and lose you valuable build time on short winter days
- The Revenue may need your IFA's assurance that the new house will be your principle residence for tax purposes. It can look as if you're building a new house to sell on, if no one addresses this issue
- In a falling property market you could lose money on your home when you come to sell up. This could threaten your new build

Rent somewhere

Pros:

- Frees up the equity in your home, perhaps to buy your plot
- Can be done close to the new house, thus allowing children to go to their new schools sooner
- Nice to start living in your new area

- Much more acceptable alternative (to many) compared with living on the site
- Cash freed from original house can be invested to help offset the cost of rent
- Can be a good way of storing your belongings....leaving few, if any, storage expenses
- Easier to convince the Revenue you own only one home
- Should be able to rent somewhere close to the site, making travelling easier and increasing your productivity

Cons:

- All rent paid is money into someone else's pocket. This makes lengthy build times very expensive
- Means taking legal advice about various types of tenancy. You must be sure you can get out of the rental agreement should you run out of cash, or complete your build earlier than expected. The temptation is to sign up for a longer agreement than you ideally want, just to be sure you won't end up on the street before your new house is ready. What I do is go for an Assured Shorthold Agreement which gives security for the first six or twelve months (whichever you agree with the landlord), with an agreed-in-writing option to continue everything on the same basis rent-wise but on a month-by-month basis once this original period is up. As I write, I am doing exactly this!
- You won't be able to keep an eye on the site's security
- You may not be able to get a mortgage when you need to

Live on site in temporary accommodation

Pros:

- It can be cheap, if you buy and sell the temporary accommodation wisely
- You're right on top of things, making it more likely you'll keep to time and budget
- You can keep a watchful eye on everything from a security point of view
- Site insurance premiums will be lower
- It's possible to take deliveries out of normal working hours when the site would otherwise be closed. This can be a fantastic advantage because rather than someone dropping an item off (or driving off with it) because there was no one around, you can check it's in good condition, left in the right place, or even put indoors, if necessary
- You can be certain of who arrives and leaves – and when...and enter the details in your site diary (see page 158)
- You can start relating to your new neighbours
- The family can get used to living in the area, with the children going to new schools
- You can go home for meals, to change clothes, and to have other creature comforts
- It can be an adventure for the whole family (provided the accommodation is comfortable!)

Cons:

- You can't get away from the job. This can be depressing when things are going badly, or if the site is a mud bath
- Friends and family could think you've lost your senses
- You will lose money on the buying and re-sale of a caravan or mobile home
- No caravan or mobile home is ever as good as living in bricks and mortar
- You'll have to spend money on storing your belongings. Rest assured that however well you plan, the very things you want will be in store! If you have good friends and a helpful family you could prevail on them to give you some storage space
- Your temporary home could get in the way of your build. It will also need planning permission and could be an eyesore for your neighbours
- You must ensure you don't trap your temporary home with your new build. Remember it has to go at the end of the day
- It'll cost to install all the essential services (telephone line, water, electricity, sewerage, water, bottled gas)

5 Designing your build

Although you might think it's easy to design a new house, especially if you've been thinking about it for a long time, you'll soon discover it's harder than you'd imagined.

First, even if you've found that nice plot, the local council's planning department will let you erect only a rather limited style of building on it. The more the property is surrounded by others, the more similar they're likely to want you to make yours. This said, increasing numbers of planners are encouraging brave, unique designs, even among other houses on streets. This is not the norm, though.

For maximum impact make your whole house into an imposing hallway....with a kitchen on the back!

It's best to talk with your designer, or even the local planning department, early on to see what they'll permit. There's no point designing a steel and glass box that everyone in the neighbourhood will object to and the planners won't go for.

The next most important thing, in my opinion, is to decide on scale. The 'mass' of a house, and how its scale compares with those around hugely influences how others perceive it. Even if you're building in an open field it's vital to get that mass right. This is a somewhat subjective thing but any good designer will guide you through the process and you'll know it when you see it. No matter if your local planners are sticklers for certain design features or materials, your designer should be able to incorporate these into a different-enough, acceptable design that will please you too.

Before going to a designer or architect (see below) it's important to know what sort of thing you have in mind, given a free hand. Work out an accommodation schedule (how many of which type of rooms) and tear out

Decide on what you want or need:

Look carefully at your current home and tell yourself what works and what doesn't, room by room. In the new place:

- How do you want to live? Most people today live in their open-plan kitchen/ family room. Is this for you?
- Will you want another, more private, space where you can be quiet, say to watch TV away from the kids?
- Do you want a utility room, or are you happy with everything in the kitchen?
- Would you like a playroom for the children?
- If you work from home, where would you like your workspace to be? Could it be in the loft, or perhaps in a separate annex with its own front door for business visitors?
- How much do you enjoy large circulation spaces? Some people ask me for a large and imposing hallway with a feature staircase, both of which give an instant wow factor as you come in the front door. Some people like wide corridors that make the place feel roomy. A generous landing is great. Grand homes of the past were characterised by their massive circulation areas. And of course they were right. Spacious parts of the house that aren't actual rooms do give a place a wonderful feel....and everyone picks up on this. Alas, all circulation space comes at a serious price and might have to be curtailed once you get your teeth into the budget. But go with it for now
- What are your hobby needs? Will they have to be accommodated indoors in a designated room or could you use a part of the garage or a large shed?
- How many bathrooms do you want? I'd suggest the master bedroom should, if at all possible, have an en-suite but after that it's a matter of taste. There should always be one bathroom (ideally not an en-suite) with an actual bath, so it can be used as a family bathroom for young children. People who try to persuade me otherwise tend to have trouble selling! Everywhere else can have showers if you like. Remember that the more bathrooms you have, the more things there are to clean and to go wrong. They're also costly features per square foot
- What was/is the best thing about any house you've ever lived in? How would you like to incorporate this into your plan?
- What were/are the worst things you've lived with? How can you be sure not to repeat them?
- Conservatories and sunrooms are very popular. How important is this sort of indoor/outdoor space to you and your family?
- How important is a garage to you? Could you miss it out altogether and not suffer? It'll save lots of money if you can
- This said, what is your need for storage, indoors and out? Most modern homes have far too little storage. Strangely, even quite good designers seem to have a blind spot on this one
- Are there things you must do outside? Will you need a pond for those Koi? Have you promised your little daughter a Wendy house?

pages from design and home décor mags to slowly build a picture of the sort of place you envisage. Get any fighting over between you and your partner before going to the architect for that first meeting. It'll help him if you provide a united front on approximately what you want. I find it hard when taking a brief from a new client couple when they spend much of the time disagreeing. It creates a bad vibe, suppresses creativity and generally holds everything up.

What, I ask myself, will they be like when we really get down to the nitty-gritty?

When planning what you think you'd like, give a thought to the future. If you're intending to make this a home for many years, think about how you'll use the place in ten or even twenty years time. Where will your adult kids stay, if they can't afford their own home? How could you accommodate Granny? What will happen once your already bad hip starts making it hard to get upstairs? And so on.

Go through the above list and, working from you own home, try to create your ideal room size for each location.

Don't forget this is just a wish list at the moment. Just go for it and see what you come up with.

If you have the patience, decide on which important pieces of furniture you really want to keep and, on squared graph paper, set out scaled, paper outlines of each, trying to create what each room might contain. Stick the 'furniture' down with BluTack so you can keep moving it around until you're happy.

If you've got the time and skill, now make scale drawings on squared paper of all this and you'll be able to start 'living' in your proposed house. Put it on a scaled plot outline, add the orientation (North/South) and see how it'll feel being in each room. Imagine the light in every room at each time of the day.

Next, make a list, in descending order, of features you'd be prepared to shave off this ideal design, when things get too expensive. I like it when people say to me, 'We'd really like the five beds but four would do and we could live without the sunroom until we get more money.' Neither sites nor budgets are elastic!

At this stage decide between you what really matters. Space or quality of finishes? Be sure you'll end up having to sacrifice one for the other at some stage, unless you have very deep pockets. Do you want a small gem, or a large, OK box? Hopefully, a good designer will be able to help you find a happy middle option but it's helpful to clarify your priorities. It's important to be true to yourselves on this or once your build is complete you'll forever feel dissatisfied. Building your own place is such a huge commitment that it's worse ending up dissatisfied than it would be living in a not-so-great spec house bought from a national house builder.

'You'll regret it' design

Hopefully, between you and your designer you'll get a nice enough outcome to please both you and the planners. But this won't be your main challenge. We live in a highly competitive world and are surrounded by endless images of domestic design perfection. This means it's all too easy to over-specify your new place – with two possible negative results. The first is that you might not be able to afford to do it at all; the second is that, once complete, it might not fit in with the other homes around you. If you have unlimited cash this won't matter. But most people don't. As you can probably rely on your self-build to make you a nice profit on your efforts of say 15%, you're ahead of the game, so to speak, the day you move in.

If you're intending to make this a home for many years, think about how you'll use the place in ten or even twenty years time

Unfortunately, this advantage can be easily lost by specifying upmarket finishes and features that, no matter how much you kid yourself, will never get you your money back. If you intend to stay in the place for the rest of your life, fine. But few people do. Some individuals get the self-build bug and sell on quite quickly. Others fall on hard times financially or health-wise. Others get divorced. And so on. Estate agents tell of torrid sessions with vendors who have over-spec'd their homes only to get angry because the agent won't recognise this film star stuff for what they see it as.

The truth is that you need only build a good enough house. Anything more is down to you

....and your bank manager. Don't imagine it will necessarily increase the value of your investment. It won't. There's a whole generation of people around today who had never seen a property crash. I've lived through two and it can be heartbreaking to see people's dream homes fetching way below what they imagined they were worth. True, they were worth it to *them* but the hard fact is that the more personalised, special, and amazing you make an average house, the more people it will put off, especially in a falling or stagnant market. Such features will limit your market and spell big money to buyers who see only more expenditure in front of them to get rid of your over-specified and over-personal design statements. They will often want this to come off your asking price.

Sorry if this all sounds rather bleak but it's a fact.

By now you'll be ready to start involving a professional designer. What are your choices?

'I see a wall of infinite thinness supporting an icosahedral, electric dome in tinted glass'

Choosing a designer

Without a doubt the average person building their new home or doing any sort of major home improvement will be able to get the design ball rolling (as I've just outlined) and even come up with some very good ideas. But, it's a very long journey from this to a set of officially-acceptable drawings that can actually be used to do the build.

Modern life is hugely complex and the rules and regulations that surround house-building are legion and tedious. In fact, few people believe me when I describe just how complicated and regulated everything is. Even after reading a book such as this you'll have only scratched the surface of what there is to know. And there's the danger that, with the best will in the world, you'll design a house which looks great on paper but which simply cannot be built!

I'll come clean. I think it's crazy not to use a design professional. Some people go it alone but the hazards are unacceptable, unless your ideas are really simple. The amount of time it will take you to learn a fraction of what's taken a professional years to master, and the effort involved in avoiding the regulatory minefields, are in itself worth paying for. And this is to assume for a moment that he'll contribute nothing to your design. Which, of course, he will.

There are four main routes to choose from.

Architect

Without doubt an architect is the best choice overall, if you want something better than ordinary. Although, as a group, architects have their drawbacks (see below) most will offer an appropriate solution to your needs.

Someone can call themselves an architect only if they are registered with the Architects' Registration Board. To get such registration you have you have undergone a training that can easily have taken seven or more years. Architects may also belong to professional institutions such as the Royal Institute of British Architects (RIBA), or similar bodies in Scotland, Wales, Northern Ireland and the Republic of Ireland.

Architects in training, spend most of their time on design. In fact most architects I know see themselves mainly as artists who create designs for work and living spaces in a somewhat aesthetic way. At one extreme of this spectrum are those designing for the commercial world on landmark buildings, who see their structures first and foremost as public sculptures! An architect's training also includes management, technical building methods, legal and contractual issues and much more. But strange though it might seem, many architects aren't that great on construction technology and pick it up as they go along. I have to say that this amazed me at first, coming to the industry as I did from a hands-on building route. The business is attractive to me largely because the process of actually making something is so rewarding. You may find your architect doesn't share your views on this. He or she could, nevertheless, still be invaluable.

The list of advantages (right) of using an architect seems compelling, but there are a couple of downsides. Going the 'architect route' is definitely the most expensive, with many charging 10% or more of the build cost. This said, fees vary hugely, as with all building professionals, and it's possible to do deals (see below).

The other disadvantage I've already alluded to. It could be that you find your architect less helpful than you'd hoped on a day-to-day building site. If you employ him to supervise (contract administer) your build, be certain he really likes and wants to do it. Checking and monitoring the nitty-gritty details on your site on a weekly (or even more frequent) basis may not be the best way to use him. If you want

An architect can:

- Look at your site and assess its viability
- Prepare design options for your consideration
- Design your house
- Prevent you from making silly mistakes that'll be hard to live with, impossible to build, or costly to remedy
- Guide you through ecological and other money-saving matters that could affect your long-term finances
- Help you decide on materials that will be acceptable to the planners
- Make models for you (or the planners), if required
- Offer 3D computer visualisations so you can really see what your place will be like to live in – possibly in the form of walk-throughs
- Send suitable drawings to the planning department
- Negotiate planning permission
- Help with planning appeals
- Ensure that what you build conforms to the required building control and planning regulations
- Oversee the tendering process and help you choose a builder
- Create a detailed specification document
- Use his network of local officials, suppliers and contacts on your behalf
- Do the drawing work and detailing required to satisfy planners and building control officials...in fact, do all necessary drawings up to and including working drawings from which your builder can actually build

BUT, most of all he can,

- Be a listening ear and an informed intermediary between the mass of officialdom and other self-interested parties that appears to be intent on preventing you getting what you want more than this an architectural technologist, surveyor, or project manager might be a better route.

Architectural technologist

This professional is a member of the British Institute of Architectural Technologists (BIAT). The training favours technical, practical and managerial issues. They are, as a result, less 'arty-farty' (design-driven, to be more polite!) than architects. If your build's design is likely to be straightforward, this can be a good route to go.

An architectural technologist can offer much of what an architect does but for a little less money, and in a more practical, nitty-gritty way.

Surveyor

I'm a fan of creative surveyors. Their training is almost entirely practical in emphasis; they solve problems well; can offer much of what an architect can (unless your design needs are great); are happy to supervise day-to-day building issues; will hold your hand if you're going to actually build the place yourself; and tend to be more acceptable to some builders. It has to be said that quite a lot of builders say architects are hard to get on with. They often find themselves trying to build something the architect hasn't thought through sufficiently well at a technical, hands-on level, even though on paper it looks great. Many builders I know find architects' drawings too complicated, too numerous, or simply impracticable.

Whilst no surveyor would pretend to be an architect, or to have their degree of design awareness, this might not be necessary if you're doing a standard house

Whilst no surveyor would pretend to be an architect, or to have their degree of design awareness, this might not be necessary if you're doing a standard house. I can highly recommend this route for those who want more than a design and drawings package for their money.

Package build companies

There are many of these, some of which will be involved in kit houses and timber-frame homes. Their great advantages are that they can provide comfort to the novice builder who will receive a fixed-price contract and will be able to see exactly what they're getting for their money before anything is built. Such outfits have teams of in-house professionals who can modify existing, off-the-shelf, plans to suit your needs. Be warned, though, that this might not turn out to be as inexpensive as you thought. I've known people pay more for this route than they would had they started from a clean sheet of paper with their own designer.

For some people there's another possible member of the design team – the interior designer. This is a trained individual who will help you decide on the way your home looks and 'feels' rather than how it's built. We're all much more aware of lifestyle issues today and interior designers can help with this at many levels. Some will act, perhaps along with an architect, to create or modify your actual building fabric, whist others will advise on how your place is kitted out.

An interior designer can help you decide on the way your home looks and 'feels' rather than how it's built

Most interior designers take a brief, just like an architect does, and then create a 'mood board', bringing together the various elements of that room or segment of your home that's being designed. This board enables you to see how things as different as curtains, painted surfaces, furniture and lighting will feel together. This is a real skill, and one that few untrained people have. It's easy for most of us to pick out a few nice things from shops but creating that overall look and mood can be very skilful. Good designers don't stop here though. They can also help you source the

'Dahling....I have just the thing!'

items you want and even get tradesmen to carry out the work to a high standard. As more of us become increasingly time-hungry I suspect we'll find ourselves using interior designers more.

Choosing a professional

Choosing the right professional can be one of your most important decisions. Here are a few thoughts:

Self-build experience. I think this is vital. If you choose a designer who'd rather work in a different way, you'll be in trouble from the start. And if you're going to actually build yourself you'll need a lot of hand-holding. Even if you use a builder you'll need someone who's prepared to take a more than usually active role in things, if only to keep a watchful eye on the builder. A problem with self-builds is that unless your builder is completely trustworthy he can be tempted to cut corners on the basis that you won't know any different – you're just too inexperienced. A professional designer with experience of self-builds will ensure you get the quality of build you are paying for while empowering you to retain overall control.

Appropriate skills and aptitude. Designing for domestic clients is a very particular skill. Many professionals simply won't do it....it's too personal, too stressful, involves too many changes of mind/heart on behalf of the clients, and so on. I was lecturing to a group of architects recently. Several came up to me afterwards and said how grateful they were that they didn't have my job! They simply didn't want to be involved with clients at such a personal level.

Where he is geographically. This is very important. It's tempting to appoint someone you may already have used, or who works a long way from your site. One of the most important things a designer can bring to the party, in my opinion, is local knowledge. If you're going to build at a distance from your existing home, as many people have to, then do your local homework and find someone who is familiar with the local planners, building control officers, builders' merchants, sources of materials, and so on. You may even find that a given designer has already been involved with the site you intend to buy. Ask around locally, perhaps even among those who are currently having houses built, to find a suitable person. It's usually a bad mistake to 'import' a design professional into an area as they can cause friction with local officials and builders and set your cause back. Local professionals, from estate agents to accountants, solicitors, engineers and council employees feel comfortable dealing with people they know, and probably drink with! This is human nature. In effect, by buying into the right designer geographically you quickly find yourself embedded in the local building fraternity....which is exactly what you'll need and want! All this applies whether your build is in a remote rural village or a suburb of a large city.

You'll need to find someone who does residential design, probably all the time, and whose design taste you like

Design style and track record. There's obviously no point talking to a professional who'd rather be designing factories! You'll need to find someone who does residential design, probably all the time, and whose design taste you like. When interviewing anyone get them to show you photos of previous work, drawings, models or whatever, so you can be satisfied that they're going to be able to do the job. My colleague and I often spend half a day or more with a potential client viewing work in progress on actual sites, along with existing homes. This is part of the business and needs to be done. At this stage we are 'interviewing' the proposed clients every bit as much as they are interviewing us, of course, so it's time well spent.

Seeing the designer in his office can tell you a lot. What's the feel of the place? Is it a mess of papers and documents? Does it feel professional? What other staff does he have around? How do they deal with you? An early visit to your proposed site will also give you clues as to how he works when presented with an actual problem.

Their personality. This is a difficult one. When you first meet your proposed designer it can be hard to know how you'll get on. Building a home or doing any other major build will be an intensely personal experience as he will need to know how you live, perhaps in a very intimate way. I've had briefings from couples who specify exactly what they want in the way of clothes storage, right down to how many underwear drawers they'll need. Others have strongly-held personal views about bathrooms, the positioning of lavatories, and so on. When you meet your designer for the first time it can be hard to tell how he'll be with the practical side of your build. Some designers (architects especially, I find) are great schmoozers, and wonderful at impressing the client, but not that great at kicking backsides to get the building work done.

Basically, you need someone who can deal well with you, listen carefully and intuitively to what you think you want, and quite quickly latch on to some sort of design ideas that will answer your needs. Some designers are loath to go straight for a sketch, because they are by nature cautious, but others like to get out a pencil and, within minutes of listening to your thoughts, start to put something on paper. This latter type is itching to visualise something, and not just for his own benefit. He knows that until most people see something in front of them they can't engage with it in their mind's eye, the way he can.

Which of these approaches appeals to you is intensely personal. And it can be hard to get right. My tendency is to rush people forward with creative ideas at this point. This is fine for some, who see it as the 'can-do' approach they're looking for, but others interpret it as too pushy and fear they'll lose control of their project. On occasions, one partner within a couple likes my approach and the other doesn't. They then have to decide between them how to proceed. This is a difficult line to tread for any design professional being approached by new clients. But when all's said and done, the designer can only be himself and if his style bothers you, go elsewhere. Bear in mind, though, that Mr Nice Guy might not be your best ally in the long run! Planning and building call for a hard head and a forceful personality. It's a fine judgement.

Until most people see something in front of them they can't engage with it in their mind's eye

References and testimonials. Any professional you'll want to deal with will be more than happy to give you a list of recent builds he's done and clients to whom you can talk. Take him up on this. Go and see the buildings he suggests and decide if they're your sort of thing. Then feed back to him. We often have people come back to us to say they didn't like what they saw, imagining this is all we can offer. Of course it isn't. So keep an open mind. Your designer may be enthusiastic to be asked to do something a little out of the ordinary for him – yet still well within his capabilities.

Next, talk to previous clients and see what they say. Talk to more than one because it could be that there was a clash of personalities and that your proposed professional will be perfectly suitable for you. Ask other local professionals too. I am frequently asked about designers I'd recommend. Because I know the low-down, my opinion can save people a lot of time and grief, especially if I know the personalities of both parties, as I often do.

Finding the right designer isn't that simple, especially if you're building in an area with which you are unfamiliar.

Luckily, the Internet has changed all this today as all the professional institutes have helpful websites. There is also an Association of Self-Build Architects. Time was when a book such as this would have contained huge lists of such addresses. Those days are gone. Just get on the Internet and put the key words into your search engine. Personal contacts are good too; local planning offices might help you; builders' merchants and local builders can also have ideas. The Yellow Pages are a last resort.

How to pay

Professional fees are a tricky issue that needs to be sorted out early in your consultation. Many of our clients raise the issue at our first meeting. All professionals will be happy to describe how they like to work and expect to be paid. And any individual designer could be open to a method of payment he doesn't usually use. Say what would suit you best and see what he thinks.

In general, designers aren't profit-centred business people who are out to rook you. They are used to working for fees, based on what they want to earn per day, as opposed to making trading profits, like a shop-keeper does.

There are four basic ways you could pay:

A lump sum. If you go this route you'll know where you stand, which might give you comfort. I personally don't like this route as I know from experience that domestic projects always call for a greater time commitment than clients imagine and that it's easy for me to lose money, or end up feeling hard done by. A way round this is to make the lump sum large enough to reflect this anticipated difficulty. But then my quote can appear very expensive compared with the quotes of others who price unrealistically to get the work hoping to make further income later when they have to charge more.

On a per-day (or per-hour) spent. This is probably fairest to everyone but means that your designer won't be able to make a windfall profit if things go better than he hoped and planned for. On the other hand, if the going gets tough, it can mean your designer's bills will rise, perhaps to alarming levels, as he spends extra time sorting out a serious problem or making significant changes you have made to your original scheme.

As a percentage of the build cost. There used to be 'scale fees' for different types of work but this system no longer operates. Under this setup professional bodies had scales of charges that pertained to different types of design work. Members of any particular professional group then billed their clients according to these fixed scales. Over recent years this method of charging has been abandoned in favour of a less restrictive arrangement.

Each client now effectively does a deal with their professional on a one-off basis, subject to the competitiveness of the market. Any individual designer will set this level at his discretion, taking into account how difficult he thinks both you and your project will be. If you're expecting the earth and the planning is likely to be near-impossible, or the actual building methods you're aiming for are exceptionally demanding, he'll price the job accordingly. He knows what can be achieved locally and can judge how challenging the project will be for him and locally-available contractors. If what you want is unrealistic, in his view, he'll tell you or he'll be totally honest and say that to even try to do it could be very costly in fees.

Problems arise, though, if you change your mind and start to escalate the build cost

A standard house shouldn't present problems to the average professional designer and he'll give you a pretty accurate idea on fees from the start. Problems arise, though, if you change your mind and start to escalate the build cost. I find this hard from a fee point of view. The client has a fee in mind (based on the original budget) but then increases the budget by say £100,000 as he increases the scope or specification. He is then unhappy about paying the additional fees that go with this. But of course there has been extra work to create this extra benefit. Other clients find it hard to accept a fee structure that is based on a percentage of costs when the building hasn't been properly specified or costed....and this could be because it's impossible to price it accurately for some time. All this calls for goodwill all round and can usually be sorted out. Be aware though that it can be a source of friction.

A percentage of the value added to the property. This system will work best when you are thinking a doing a self-build to sell on. Some designers will be happy to become involved on a sort of partnership basis, where they stand to make a profit on the venture, along with you. If it's just a home for you to live in, I wouldn't go this route.

The next step

Once you've selected your designer and shown him your own efforts at the design, it's time for him to get to work. Before he starts he'll want some sort of contract. He'll have a standard one he usually uses. Don't imagine that by signing this you'll give up control over your project...you won't. You should also clarify with him that you'll be able to get out of the contract at any time (subject to paying him for his efforts to date), if you find things aren't working, for whatever reason. This contract will usually be divided into Stage Payments that are due to him at very specific steps on the design/planning/build ladder. This makes it possible for you to plan your finances and not get any nasty surprises.

Now is the time to give your designer a detailed brief as to what exactly it is you want. He'll take your notes and preliminary floor plans (see page 41) and examine them carefully. He'll then ask you lots of questions. I always like to go to a new client's home at this stage, to see how they live. This can provide valuable clues about things they haven't articulated....after all, they see the way they live as 'normal', as we all do.

The next stage is known in the business as 'developing the design'. Here the designer gets his creative juices going and starts to flesh out, either on paper or on CAD (an electronic, computer-based design programme), his initial solution to your brief. He might come up with something – or indeed several ideas – that are radical, compared with what you had in mind. Go gently, and rule nothing out until you've given him a chance to have his say. After all, if you'd been able to do this process yourself, you wouldn't have hired him.

Your wish list is now subjected to scrutiny as its inconsistencies and impossibilities come to light. You can't, for example, have those picture windows that can't be opened in your master bedroom, dramatic though they'd be, because fire regulations just won't allow it. And so on. Take this criticism as it's meant but challenge him when you feel you should. A good designer should be pushing your envelope. This can appear challenging but is the surest way to end up with something that's better than good.

Unfortunately this process isn't a straight line, which can frustrate people of a certain personality type. Imagine a 'design spiral'. You are now at the first (base) turn. As the weeks or months go by you'll ascend the spiral revisiting the same issues time and again until you eventually arrive at something your designer, you, the planners, the building control people, your builder, and other key stakeholders accept. It's important to keep an open mind and be patient, especially as the time between turns of the spiral could be weeks or months, if planning is difficult.

When all's said and done, there are huge numbers of possible solutions to most

'Heaven knows how I'll incorporate this chaos and clutter into the new design'

domestic design challenges. There are few 'right' answers. The secret of working well with a designer is to use their professional skill to get what you think you want while keeping them on-board so they remain enthusiastic, even passionate, about your project.

This brings me to the matter of 'ownership'. From your point of view the proposed house is 'yours'. It's your idea, it's your money and it's your family that'll live in it. From your designer's point of view it is 'his'. And your builder will also consider it to be 'his'. This can be difficult for the first-time self-builder as everybody seems to think his baby is theirs! But viewed in the right way this is a vital advantage. What you want is all your professionals seeing the project as theirs so they claim professional ownership....and thus give it the care and passion it deserves. If you insist on holding everything close to your chest you'll lose many of the advantages of team ownership and by doing so you'll lose a lot. To get the best possible outcome, everyone involved needs to feel they're investing something of themselves in your build.

Your designer will by now have some floor plans, elevations, site plans, preliminary specifications and so on to discuss with you. Now, over several weeks, you'll refine all these until you are all happy. Then you'll sign them off so he can take matters to the next stage. This is your last chance to satisfy yourself that all is well and to speak out if it isn't. This is important because thus far it's all been a rather cosy club consisting of you and your designer. The next stage takes all this into the public arena of building regulations and planning and things are set for a whole new mind-set. In parallel with this 'pre-planning' phase someone will need to draw up a specification for your build.

6 Specification – the secret of success

Specifying is the process in the run-up to a build during which a list is drawn up of everything that has to be sourced, and detailed in a formal way. From this highly specific schedule a builder or quantity surveyor can accurately cost your project.

This detailed 'spec' can be drawn up by your designer or a quantity surveyor employed by him or you. It details everything from the start of the work on the site to the very last job to be done. It lists everything to do with Health and Safety Regulations and all kinds of other regulatory considerations, because every single one of these will have a cost....and it'll be you who foots the bill.

You can safely leave the specification of the structural and actual 'building' matters to your professionals but you'll have to take an active hand in everything else.

This means specifying lots of things and making masses of choices. For example, your designer (and the planners) say they'd like a brick finish to the building. But there are thousands of different types of brick. Which to choose? Which will look best with a particular type of slate on the roof? What colour mortar will look best with that brick? What colour window frames will look best with that brick? And so it goes on. This stage could see you going to the proposed brick company, or at the least to a brick 'library' to make an informed decision. Every such choice has a cost implication which will have to be looked at carefully and decisions made.

As I say to clients all the time, 'The more you can nail down at this stage the more accurate your costings will be and the safer everyone will feel with your build.' In an ideal world we should specify everything exactly the way it will be, long before anything gets near to being built. Listen to your designer and be guided by his experience. This said, only you know how you want to live, so when it comes to things that will affect your actual use of the house (such as the electrical specification), be sure to have your say in some detail.

The more you can nail down at this stage the more accurate your costings will be and the safer everyone will feel with your build

Give your designer a list such as the one below to help him on his way. It should be accompanied by a drawing on which you have marked all the positions of the wall sockets, and electrical fittings (including lighting locations) etc. Don't be afraid to make mistakes. He'll take you through everything carefully and discuss the pros and cons of what you want. He can then draw up the final

SAMPLE ELECTRICAL SPECIFICATION

All switch-plates, sockets etc to be in white plastic made by XXX
All 13Amp sockets to be doubles
All lights controlled by simple switches except for dimmer to Dining Room pendant
All TV sockets to have phone socket adjacent

Exterior of house

Exterior lighting on house: 4No outlets. Fittings supplied by us
2No outside water-proof sockets around terraces as shown
Power supply to shed
Power supplies for 2No lighting bollards on parking area (fittings supplied by us)
Power supply to 2No pillar lights at front entrance (fittings supplied by us)
Power supply to front gate, in case we want to make it electric one day

House

Bed 2
13A sockets: 4No doubles
Lighting: 6No recessed spots (down lighters model X by XXX)
Lighting in wardrobes: 2No, (type B by BBB) on door switches.
TV sockets: 2No
Additional phone sockets: 2No
Smoke detector

Bath 2
Lighting: 3No down lighters (one of which over bath...water-proof type)
Mirror light (model C by CCC)
Shaver point
Extractor fan

Hall
13A Sockets: 2No
Lighting: 6No down lighters
Phone sockets: 1No
Smoke detector

Utility
3No 13A below worktop for washer; dryer etc
2No 13A above worktop
Lighting: 1No fluorescent double
Power for central heating gear/pumps etc
1No further 13A supply on south wall, as marked

Study
13A Sockets: 3No in main room plus 4No in office area
Lighting: Single source for central pendant (supplied by us) in main room, 4No down lighters to office area
TV: 1No each in room plus 1No each in office area
Phone sockets: 1No in room plus 1No in office area
Additional phone socket in main room

Kitchen
Lighting: 6No down-lighters
4No 13A Power points above worktop
3No sources for cooker/fridge/hob
Heat sensor
1No Phone socket
Extractor over cooker (model P by PPP)

Dining
13A Sockets: 4No
Lighting: Central pendant over table, controlled by dimmer. Pendant supplied by us

Lounge
13A Sockets: 2No wall plus 4No set into floor
Lighting: together with Dining Room: 10No down lighters under flat roof areas
1No TV with satellite source
1No additional phone socket

Bed 1
13A Sockets: 4No
Lighting: 6No down lighters
Lighting in wardrobes: 2No ceiling sources with door switches
1No TV
Additional phone sockets: 1No

Bath 1
Lighting: 4No down lighters, of which 1No in shower (waterproof)
Shaver point
Mirror lights: 2No, one either side of main mirror (model K, by KKK)
Extractor fan

Stairs
6No down lighters
2No 13A Sockets on landing

Loft
2No 1.8m fluorescent fittings, switched from landing, with tell-tale switch on landing

General
Burglar alarm....first fix only. We will arrange for my uncle's alarm company to do second fix

specification ready for pricing. If you're not sure how much detail is needed, ask your designer. He'll be able to fill in various gaps you leave, perhaps after consulting with the contractor who'll do the work.

From this sort of detail your designer can see exactly how you want to live and begin to suggest changes or modifications that could make life better for you and/or reduce the cost. His modifications to this level of specification then form the basis of the document that your electrical contractor will price on. As you can see, little is left to doubt and everyone knows where they stand from day one.

You now need to repeat this process for:

- Plumbing, heating and sanitary fittings
- Internal doors and door furniture
- Kitchen/utility room units, white goods and fittings
- Staircase and balustrade
- Internal wall surfaces/finishes and coving
- Floors and their finishes
- Ceramic tiling everywhere
- Internal decorations
- External windows and doors
- Exterior surfaces of roof and walls
- Rainwater goods
- External decorations
- Paving, footpaths, driveway, patio surfaces, and decking
- Planting and landscaping

Clearly, this is a huge job! It can take several weeks to complete. But it can only be done by you as the home owner, because only you can know how you want to live and what you can afford. Unless and until the specification is created to this level of accuracy no one can claim to know how much your build will cost.

All this can sound terribly daunting but a good designer will be a great help. He should have all kinds of brochures and professional sources to which he can refer you to see items on which he'll need your decision. He'll have his favourite things that he has used time and again and knows to be what you're looking for.

'Do we *have* to re-use this?'

If you find any of this specifying stage too much, ask your designer to help. For example, he won't expect you to provide a detailed specification of your central heating boiler. This said, you may have very strong views on eco issues and want him to specify a special boiler. Detail and specify everything you reasonably can, or care to, and leave the rest to him.

At this stage you'll be surfing the web and spending many a happy weekend looking at stoves, taps, or whatever! It makes sense when doing this to look at and price not just what you think you want (which may well be too expensive when you come to add everything up) but also to consider cheaper options while you're at it, to save going back. Take lots of photos of things as you search....your memory will play tricks after seeing 30 baths.

As you can see, specifying is a disciplined activity that takes a massive amount of time and energy. If you have neither, you can always get your designer, or a colleague of his who specialises in specifying, to do all the donkey work for you. This obviously costs money but your time may be more valuable. For many self-builders, though, the fun of doing all this research is an integral part of the project. Some say they like the thrill of the chase and take a joy in doing deals that save them money. However, a professional specifier has many sources of just about everything at his finger-tips and can do a lot in a short time compared with you starting from scratch. He'll also come up with ideas you'd never have thought of. It's up to you how you want to play this but however it's done and whoever does it, drawing up the spec is a vital part of the process of any build.

Only you can know how you want to live and what you can afford

7 Building Regulations and the planning system

Many people say how amazed they are at the complexity and sheer amount of regulations involved with what they thought would be a simple matter....building a small family home or an extension.

The truth is that all over the western world the picture is much the same, with a very few exceptions. Governments everywhere have passed legislation that controls building methods and other related issues. It is simply impossible to construct a house ignoring this regulatory stuff. Believe it or not, there are countries where the rules are even more strict than in the UK.

There are two distinct but inter-related sets of legislation in the UK and the Republic of Ireland....though both are slightly different as each jurisdiction is, of course, autonomous.

The first is Planning and the second, Building Regulations (Regs). I'll look at planning first as this is the more difficult of the two and without it you won't have a building to be regulated!

Planning

This is the first part of fulfilling your statutory requirements when building. But just as satisfying Building Control doesn't give you planning permission, you cannot build, once planning has been authorised, unless your building regs are in order.

Of these two issues, though, planning is the vastly more difficult and stressful, and calls for the most skill.

Planning can appear very confusing and inconsistent. People frequently ask me how a system based on laws can be so haphazard. The reasons are that each local council makes up its own rules, and individuals within the planning department interpret these rules differently. This means that certain planning departments favour certain types of design, development in rural areas, changes of use, etc that others in a neighbouring area wouldn't even contemplate. Within any one Department you could, in addition, have a particular planning officer who takes a dislike to certain architectural features and styles and makes life hard for you. Another officer in the same department might rule differently. On top of all this, national (as opposed to local) government rulings on planning on a national scale can over-rule certain local planning laws. Obviously, such regulations fluctuate with changes of government policy over the years.

There's an impressive list of issues that your designer and the planners will take into account when considering your planning application. Any one of these could mean failure, so they must be considered thoroughly. This will make up the majority of the work your designer does for you at this stage. Given that about one in three planning applications submitted in the UK is rejected,

General considerations:

- What the local Development Plan will allow...the 'Bible' planners usually have to follow. This can be viewed on line
- What current local politics dictate. This is inevitably an area of shifting sands!
- Statutory limitations imposed on: Listed buildings, development in conservation areas and in areas of outstanding natural beauty, national parks etc
- Central government rulings....there are changes in the air all the time
- The planning history of the site. I tend to choose sites with 'planning histories', which immediately impose a burden on the system as they often come with a 'bad smell'. In exchange for hard work at overcoming negative planning issues great gains can be made if you are successful where others have not been. It'll pay you to be very familiar indeed with the planning history of your proposed development
- Development out of keeping with the neighbourhood. This is worth a fight as some planners in certain areas become more adventurous over time

the more effectively you prepare your case, the more likely your success. There are two sets of considerations. The first governs planning matters in general, the second, your particular proposal.

Taking all the above considerations into account, your designer should have provided everything the local council's planning department needs to obtain your permission. Once they have all this, the matter is in the public domain. Anyone can now look at your proposals and comment on them. This takes your build into a whole new realm, as until now it'll have been a somewhat private affair between you and your designer. Emotions now start to rise as the planners (who are paid to do it) and various other parties (who aren't) start to question your plans. It can be hard to remain unaffected by this process. I think it's best to distance yourself as much as you can from all this and let your professional do his job. Things that may sound terrible to you could just be par for the course. Your professional should be able to shield you from the various to-ings and fro-ings.

Planning laws

Planning laws originate both locally and nationally. Ordinary planning issues are dealt with by local authorities (councils) but complex ones and appeals are dealt with at a higher (national) level. In general, decisions about plannings are made in accordance with the local council's Development Plan....a sort of master plan that is reviewed every few years and governs all planning in a 'general-principles' sort of way that balances the area's

Issues specific to your design:

- 'Mass' of house too large in the context of neighbouring buildings
- Too little parking
- Not enough space for cars to turn on site
- Poor exit visibility of, and from, public road
- Overlooks neighbours too much
- Bad position on plot
- Roof line too high
- Basement not allowed
- Garden too small (site over-developed)
- Poor choice of external materials
- Robs neighbours of too much light
- Involves removing too many trees or hedges
- Threat to wildlife
- Archaeological remains
- Liability to flooding
- Can't supply adequate private sewage disposal
- Contaminated ground
- Adversely affects rights of way
- Objections from local community
- Precedents for something like your design

needs for shopping, recreation, schooling, industry, commerce, housing, employment, tourism and so on. This master plan won't, for example, allow you to build a multi-storey car park or a nursery school in your suburban street as part of your new home!

This doesn't mean that something you want cannot be accommodated if it falls outside this Plan but it's uncommon. Such out-of-the-ordinary plannings need to have 'material considerations' taken into account before they can be permitted.

Very obviously, a major part of any local authority's planning policy includes housing. Where new housing is to be encouraged, the conversion/extension/rehabilitation of existing buildings, and the numbers of new homes that should be built in villages, are all the sorts of things that local planners will have given a lot of thought to and seek to regulate. All councils have rules about in-filling between and behind existing houses, and on house extension and replacement. Most have green belt rules (so homes don't sprawl along ribbon developments into the countryside), and so on. Much of this information is available on the internet but I always go by my designer's experience on this if working in an unfamiliar area of the country. Things can be surprisingly different from place to place and it's unwise to make assumptions from past experience. Life's too short to have to learn everything from scratch in a new area, when your designer has it all at his fingertips. Most important, not only will he know the planning laws but he'll know the wrinkles of how they're interpreted. This is what you want. If you really insist on reading things up for yourself, the local library or your council's planning website will help guide you to the information you'll need.

The list on the opposite page is certainly not exhaustive. If in any doubt, ask a professional

'Are you sure the sunken bath is this deep?'

or check with your local council's planning office. Visit www.planningportal.gov.uk and use their 'Visual guide for Homeowners' to be sure you don't need permission.

It is possible to apply for planning permission yourself. As you'll have gathered by now, I don't advise this except in the most simple of circumstances or if you have loads of time and energy that couldn't, or shouldn't, be better spent doing something else. The point is this: if everything really is simple, no fair-minded professional will charge you all that much, but if it isn't you stand little chance of navigating the minefields yourself and will need professional help eventually anyway.

Depending on where you live (and the Republic of Ireland has somewhat different rules), you could need planning permission for some or any of the following, provided they are not covered by Permitted Development (see page 97):

- A new house
- Extending
- Conservatories and sunrooms
- All demolition
- Loft conversions
- Dormer windows and changes to your roof structure
- Anything involving a listed building (other legislation applies too)
- Changing the use of a building (agricultural to domestic, for example)
- Garages
- Porches
- Making a basement
- Building a swimming pool
- Enclosing balconies
- Making additions or extensions to a flat or maisonette
- Dividing off part of a home for business use
- Making a separate bed-sit
- A new house in your garden
- Changing the planning permission that applies already to your house
- Changing your access to the public road
- Installing a mobile home while you build on a new site
- Sheds
- Greenhouses
- Satellite dishes and TV aerials

Applying for planning permission

If you do go the DIY route, here's what to do: Visit your local planning department and start to create a relationship with the office. You can get the name of the planner who deals with your area by giving them your post code.

Write a letter that says clearly what you want to do; include photos of your place and neighbouring houses; and take a scale diagram you've done of the proposed development. Whether you now discuss your ideas over the phone with a planner or get to see someone in planning in person with this material, ask whether or not your scheme requires planning permission. Things are changing in the UK on pre-planning meetings. The new, nation-wide, on-line planning form has a specific question relating to pre-application advice. Most councils now offer free pre-planning advice to householders. This said, such advice may not take place in person. Things differ from council to council. Once an application is submitted, however, they will not subsequently enter into dialogue with an applicant or their agent. This makes it sensible to go for a pre-planning meeting whenever a project looks the slightest bit contentious. Take along as much as you reasonably can so your meeting is as valuable as it can be. If you walk in off the street you'll only get a clerical officer, who will, in all honesty, be able to give only very simple, factual answers. A formal meeting will mean you sit face to face with a planning officer.

My experiences of many planning officers over the years are that they vary from hugely helpful, serious-minded professionals, to annoying, self-appointed social manipulators who clearly went into the job to engineer a better society (according to their definitions).

From what I've just said, I think it's plain that even if you do get a pre-planning meeting you won't get a decision on anything. And this is not unreasonable. The person you see will have only very limited information (supplied by you, who can't be the most impartial individual in the circumstances), and they'll never have seen the site, though, in my experience, they'll probably know of it. What they *can* do is to guide you on the biggest issues and difficulties and hopefully prevent you going down entirely unsuitable paths. This said, a local designer worth his salt could do all this for a small fee and do so in a personalised way that could suit you better.

Most councils now offer free pre-planning advice to householders

Whether you've had a pre-planning meeting or talked over matters on the phone with a planner, you'll now have to go through the correct steps to lodge your application correctly. This involves:

Filling in all the application forms (bearing in mind that huge numbers of such forms are filled in wrongly, holding everything up, sometimes for weeks). You can download these from your planning department's website or get them at the Planning Department. Some departments also have useful guidance notes.

Supplying all the right paperwork, including: A location plan; site layout plan; floor plans of each floor; elevations; two cross-sectional drawings; and photographs of the site and its neighbours. You also need to send in an Ownership Certificate which shows that you are the owner of the property. If you're doing a conversion, show an 'as is' plan to make it clear how you intend to alter things. If you are intending to use a sewerage treatment plant you'll also have to supply percolation test results to prove that your land is suitable for such an installation.

Even if you are using a professional I suggest you check all this paperwork for yourself as errors occur all the time.

The council should acknowledge your application in writing within a few days and it will be placed on their Planning Register so it can be inspected by anyone who wants to. It might be advertised in the local paper, to bring it to wider public attention. In the Republic of Ireland all planning applications are publicly advertised.

The sort of time-line to expect for planning applications in England and Wales is:

Written confirmation that you've filled in the forms correctly	1 week
Consultation period (during which a sign appears on your site and possibly a notice in the local paper so people can have their say)	3 weeks
Consideration period, in which the planning officer looks everything through and considers objections	2 weeks
Recommendation (what the planners decide)	2 weeks

These are the desired times but the planning wheels can grind at their own pace according to the departmental workload and the complexity of your proposition. Eventually you'll be entitled to see the working papers from all the parties involved (including any objectors). How much you should pester the planners throughout this waiting period is up for debate. People are usually anxious to know how things are progressing and call to enquire when something will happen and whether or not it looks like going through. This is yet another reason for using a professional. They know when to push and when to leave things. They are familiar with the natural rhythm of their local planners and won't want to annoy them. Planners with whom I've discussed this

Don't make enemies of local politicians

find it irritating to have endless calls from people for whom there are, as yet, no answers. When they are busy with an onerous workload this is the last thing they want.

Planning officials eventually come to their decision or involve the council's planning committee (which then has the final say). Straightforward decisions don't go to the committee but if a planner receives lots of public objections; a councillor requests a committee meeting; or if public or highly contentious issues are involved, the committee will be asked to decide. The committee, which in most areas sits once a month, usually follows the recommendations of its professional staff.

This whole process is supposed to take about eight weeks, but can take longer. If you don't have a decision within this time, you can appeal. You have three months in which to do this. Appeals are to be avoided if possible as they take months and can be very stressful, especially if you opt for the legal route. It's always best to change your proposals, if you can, to take into account what the planners want. Of course, at worst you could even abort and sell your site on.

Lobbying

If you think your planning could hit problems it makes sense to lobby local councillors, to get them on your side. This is extremely common in Ireland, where I work a lot. Local MPs (known as TDs in the Republic) or councillors frequently take up the planning cause of a constituent, often with good results. Ideally such lobbying is done before you apply for planning in the first place but if you appeal it can be used to get a change of decision.

Lobbying neighbours is always worth the time. They'll be told of your plans officially by the council anyway but it's decent to inform them first. Try to see as many of them as you can face to face or, failing that, put a letter through their doors outlining your plans. How about arranging a get-together at the local pub, or your home if you live locally, so everyone can have their say? Make it plain you're keen to listen to them (see page 16) and that your interest is in improving the local area, not wrecking it. Listening to any objections will greatly help your designer plan his approach, so even a somewhat hostile meeting need not be time wasted.

A few helpful letters from neighbours to the planning committee can work wonders. If you have local supporters, as soon as you have the planning reference and the name of the officer handling the case, get your allies writing in. More to the point, if you have a critical number of local objectors your case will have to go to the Planning Committee rather than be decided by an Officer.

Listening to any objections will greatly help your designer plan his approach

Whether you are trying for a planning permission yourself, or going through a designer, there are two possible routes.

Outline planning

Rather than going straight to a full planning, it can make sense to apply for outline planning permission. Many building plots are sold with outline permission, which simply means that there has been a decision to allow a house of a particular general description to be built. You can't usually go this route in a conservation area. The issues that are not included in this type of permission are called Reserved Matters. They all have to be sorted out later when you go for Full Planning Permission. Go for Outline if you aren't sure exactly what you want to do on your site, or if you have a site you want to sell on. Obviously your full planning application cannot substantially alter the original, Outline, scheme. For example, you can't usually change the permission given at the outline planning stage from a small bungalow into a three-storey family home.

Full planning

If you're buying a plot with full planning, get sight of the actual planning permission as soon as you can. Estate agents usually have copies to look at while you're considering the purchase. You might want to change what has been permitted. If such changes are small the planners may well take a view and allow them. If they are at all major, though, you could have to go through the whole planning process again. Some mortgage sources insist on full planning before they'll lend.

As the planning applies to the site and not the owner, you can always make use of someone else's planning but you can't use their house plans without getting permission from their designer. His name and contact details will be on the drawings. Technically and legally, house plans belong to their designer. Even when you have paid for your designs, all you are buying is the equivalent of a licence to use those plans for your own house. He, on the other hand, can sell these same plans to someone else again. The design is his copyright, not yours.

Some mortgage sources insist on full planning before they'll lend

All planning decisions have a limited lifespan. A full planning insists that you must start work within five years of the permission (though it is said this could soon change to three). With outline permission you have only three years to submit your final design, then a further two years once you've started the work. If you, or someone else, has let the allotted time lapse you may be able to get planning permission again but this is by no means certain. Local councils and even central government are notoriously subject to political change and attitude. What was acceptable a few years ago may now not be, and vice versa. These are shifting sands upon which you cannot build with any certainty. Your designer will be familiar with all this and may even have been involved in creating (or previously fighting) some of it.

Planning conditions

Although the day you get your planning permission will be a time for celebration, read everything very carefully because almost all permissions come with Conditions....some of which can be very nasty. Go through all of them with your adviser so as to be sure of the implications of each and every one of them. You must not go ahead unless you are certain you'll be able to comply with these conditions. And complying with some could be very hard, expensive, or even impossible. It's now you'll need a steady professional hand to guide you, one who has seen such conditions before and knows what they really mean in your area.

Common Planning Conditions include:

- Time limit before planning expires (usually five years)
- Times for starting and finishing work each day
- The materials you must use externally
- Modifications to site access (which could be difficult, or even impossible)
- Planting/landscaping requirements
- Limits on what can ever be built on your site other than your (proposed) home (for example, no houses in the garden later on!)
- Limits to occupation (say, in rural areas, to agricultural workers)
- Supplying a private sewage treatment plant if you're off the main sewer
- Limits to how much you'll ever be able to extend the house at a later date

It's at this stage that your trusted designer could be worth his weight in gold. Fighting some of these conditions might be costly but could just save the whole project.

Appeals

Given that about one third of all planning applications are refused, what's a self-builder to do? The obvious thing is to give up and try somewhere else! But few of us planning a self-build quit this easily.

If you are refused planning you'll automatically be sent details of how to appeal

The reasons for refusal come mainly from my lists on page 56. Sometimes the refusal will be justified but if you've had the help of a good professional it's unlikely you'll have made silly mistakes. So there could be a good case for an appeal.

If you don't want to give up, you have two options. Alter things to please the planners (perhaps with the help of a planning consultant), or go for an entirely new planning application. In theory (and indeed in practice) you can try for a new planning while appealing the failed one. There's no fee for submitting an appeal but it'll delay you by at least six months. If you are refused planning you'll automatically be sent details of how to appeal. Ask your designer if he is experienced in handling appeals. If he is not, ask him to suggest someone who is. There are planning consultants who do little else than handle appeals. Such an individual may advise you straight away not to bother.

Whatever you decide to do (apart from give up), do everything you can to show that you have tried to be reasonable; have done your best to go along with your council's planning regulations; and are trying hard to find a compromise. If you feel aggrieved, frustrated, angry or aggressive, get these emotions out of the way in the presence of your professional advisers. Never let them loose on anyone involved in your appeal.

There are three types of appeal procedure:

Written representation: Here you present your case (or get your 'agent' to do so), saying clearly why you think you've been wrongly refused. On a due date, an inspector will visit the site then decide on his ruling.

Everything is in writing, there are no meetings in person.

Informal hearing: This method is used when it's important to meet on site. You and/or your adviser can meet the inspector on site to talk it all through. It's an approach that takes several months longer than the written version and costs can be awarded.

Public enquiry: I've taken this route and it's not pleasant. It is viable only when there's a point of law or a very difficult planning matter at stake. The written stages are followed by a courtroom-like situation, perhaps with specialist legal representation. I found the cross-examination somewhat gruelling, I have to say, when I went to such an appeal. Barristers cost lots of money, so the whole case has to be worthy of such an outlay.

Changes to the planning system

As this book went to press in late 2008, Permitted Development legislation was changed. I look at these in detail on page 70.

Another change in the offing is the UK government's plan to introduce a Community Infrastructure Levy by Spring 2009. Extensions and minor alterations won't be affected but self-built homes certainly will be. The charge will in effect be a tax on the uplift in value of your land once you get planning permission for your house. This new Levy will be most felt by those living in areas where there currently isn't a Section106 Agreement on single home building projects. The new Levy will be payable on starting your build, so be prepared to have the cash ready.

> **Anyone who intends to build has to ensure that the work is approved**

Those of us who develop in Ireland have been used to a system like this for some years. It severely sticks in the throat in rural areas, though, where the 'infrastructure' is poor...no street lighting, free rubbish collections, community water supply, mains sewers, and so on.

Building Regulations (Regs)

These make up a set of laws that ensures all buildings are made to be safe. It applies to all building work, not just homes. Over recent years this 'build it so it doesn't fall down' principle has been massively enhanced year after year to include all manner of other issues (see below). Anyone who intends to build a house has to ensure that the work is approved by one of two acceptable sets of people: the Building Control service provided by the local council, or a similar service provided by approved inspectors. You must get approval or you could have to remove what you've built.

If you don't want to use your local authority's building control people, you can find a suitably trained (but more expensive) person by asking around your professional advisers or your builder; looking on your council's website; or going to www.labc.co.uk, the official site of local authority building control. Even if you think you might be exempt from building control, be sure to take advice. This isn't something you can afford to get wrong. Get the advice confirmed in writing from whomever you deal with.

Whichever route you choose, the trained individual will offer their opinion on what you intend to construct way before building starts. The legal responsibility for the work is down to the individual (or building company) who does it. On a self-build, this will be you. If you use a builder as your main contractor, he will carry the can. This fact should be clarified in your contract with him.

But your builder won't be the only one who takes responsibility for the building regs. Many regs apply to plumbing, electrics, working with gas, and windows, for example. It makes sense to employ only those subcontractors and professionals who are qualified to carry out such work. Such an individual is technically known as a 'competent person' and can sign off on their work as compliant with the required regs. For example, if you choose a particular window company, they'll have done their homework to be sure your new windows are up to the necessary regs.

The building regulation 'requirements' usually form an integral part of your designer's drawings, or additional notes. He will know the local building control people and how best to present things in a way they like. He'll also know, from experience, how they prefer to overcome local problems (such as foundations in blue clay, for example). This knowledge can greatly reduce the time it takes to obtain Building Control Approval for your building work.

Building Regs are published as separate booklets called 'Approved Documents'. Each Part has its own letter (though these are different in Scotland, to confuse matters) and you can buy all 14, or a cheaper digest, from HMSO publications. This latter is called Home Builder and is written for small house builders.

You can download everything free from www.communities.gov.uk This said, most good builders (and I myself) have never read these documents in their entirety. We rely on the designer doing his job professionally and the building inspector giving guidance when needed.

'Building work' according to the Act that governs building regs includes:

- Erection or extension of a building
- Underpinning of a building
- Insertion of cavity wall insulation
- Changes to installations or services already in place and covered by the legislation
- Alterations to existing buildings that could affect any of the regulations

The Parts of the Building Regulations (England and Wales)

Part A	Structure
Part B	Fire
Part C	Waterproofing
Part D	Cavity insulation
Part E	Sound
Part F	Ventilation
Part G	Hygiene
Part H	Drains and fuel
Part J	Flues and chimneys
Part K	Stairs
Part L	Energy use
Part M	Access and facilities for the disabled
Part N	Glazing
Part P	Electrics

In case you think all this sounds unnecessary, it isn't. Your mortgage source will demand a completion certificate issued by the Building Control Officer and when you come to sell, your buyer's solicitor will certainly want to be sure the house has been built to standard or he'll advise his client to back out.

Rather than my listing all the exceptions to the general rule that all new building work needs to comply with this legislation, talk to your local Building Control Department, tell them about your project, and they'll advise you. Strange to tell (given this is all grounded in law), each local Building Control Department has its own ways of interpreting various matters...and it is not unknown for each individual inspector to have his own quirks of interpretation. Don't fight this; just go along with what they say.

Getting approval

It is the job of your local Building Control Department to carefully look through all the drawings and proposals they receive for new building work. They then, in return for a fee, offer advice, come to your site at various pre-planned stages of the build, and, finally, issue a completion certificate to say that all is what it should be. The NHBC and some other private companies can also fulfil this role (see above).

Ask your designer which route is best for your build.

On inspection of the information sent by your designer, the Building Control Department may ask for further work or clarification. A common example is to ask you to appoint a structural engineer to provide calculations on foundations, structural beams, and so on. Once this is all passed, the inspector dealing with your case will let you know in writing that your application has been accepted. This is an encouraging milestone on your build journey but, just to avoid any confusion, let me say this has absolutely nothing to do with getting planning permission, as some people imagine.

If your building control application is rejected, your designer will take matters in hand and resubmit things so as to satisfy the building regs people. This might mean modifying the design in some way, so you could be involved once more.

There is another way of getting regs approval but I don't advise it for any but the most able of self-builders. This is known as a 'building notice'. Here, you submit no drawings or documents but get straight on with your build, having given the authorities due notice of a commencement date. You're very unlikely to do this with a new house but I have had to go this route on several occasions for lesser works. The gamble is that once the inspector does come, he or she could find your work unacceptable and may make you undo it. As you can see, this is not a route for the first-timer, or anyone of a nervous disposition!

Most local authorities take between three and six weeks to complete your Approval. It's unwise to start any building work until this permission comes through, though I usually get on with site clearance and even demolition. You absolutely should not dig any foundations until you get clearance.

I've already said that your inspector will come to the site at pre-planned stages. These are fairly standard but can be modified at any time if the inspector feels further supervision is needed. By and large these inspectors are seasoned professionals who can be really helpful if you approach them in the right way. What they are not is a free building advice service, and they won't teach you how to

A meeting over drinks with the neighbours can get them on your side

build! This said, over the years, some inspectors have been really helpful to me whilst others have been 'by-the-rules' people who appeared to make life difficult. Try, whatever you do, to get the best out of them.

Your Building Control Inspector will usually come:

- On Commencement (the day you start on your site...though this is flexible)
- Once your foundations are dug
- To inspect your concrete being poured into the foundations
- At ground floor concrete slab stage
- To inspect your damp-proof course
- To check foul water drainage
- On completion of your roof
- On completion of the whole build

You'll notice that none of this above list involves anything to do with plumbing, electrics and so on. These inspectors are largely interested in structural matters and other things that are governed by the various parts (see page 62) of the regs. A word of warning here. These regs change all the time....even sometimes 'behind your designer's back', as it were. Your inspector will ensure that everyone is up to speed on the latest regs.

Building Control Inspectors

So he or she can know when you are 'Commencing' the project, you must give them at least a week's notice, preferably two. When they come on this initial day they'll usually be seeing your site for the first time and will start to comment on anything that concerns them.

On one of my sites this commencement visit led to a change of foundation design when the inspector deemed that a tree was closer to the foundations than he felt was safe. This meant going for structural advice, but in the end we settled on a much deeper trench (and several thousands of pounds in extra digging and concrete). With any luck such events will be rare. But bear in mind that no matter what your designer or other professionals may have advised, the inspector can simply over-rule their judgement and make you comply with what he wants. This isn't much fun as you watch a bathroom's worth of cash pouring into the ground! But it won't just be more concrete, of course. There'll be more digging, more muck-away lorries and even possibly shoring up the trench walls as the dig becomes dangerous. Did I say *one* bathroom?

No matter what your designer or other professionals may have advised, the inspector can simply over-rule their judgement and make you comply with what he wants

This first visit can be a good time to get your designer and/or the builder along. This starts the collaborative team-building you'll need. The inspector will almost certainly know them both and with luck you'll be off to a good start. But keep your eyes open and your senses peeled. This early meeting can provide useful information about both designer and builder. I've detected all kinds of interesting things on watching how the inspector deals with key personnel. On one occasion it become clear that the inspector had fallen out with the builder in the past and that she'd be keeping a very watchful eye on him. This helped me be more cautious too. And it paid off.

I like to get my setting out done by this visit so the inspector can have their say. If you want to change the location of the building a little, this is the time to say so. If this change is anything but very minor, though, it could cause long delays as you might have to go for planning again.

Although this isn't a building manual I think it's wise to point out a few things that will impact on your inspector's visits.

Excavations: Because foundations are so vital to the building of a safe house or extension the dig inspection is very important. Your groundworkers will have dug out to an appropriate depth, removing uncertain soil where they think necessary (even if it meant going deeper than planned), to get to a solid base. Your builder's experience will help him a lot on this, as he'll be aware of the soil types in the vicinity and know what the inspector is likely to accept.

If the trenches are cleanly cut; if there are no signs of roots coming through the sides; if they are cleaned out at the base; and if the dimensions and positioning on the site are as they should be; the inspector will give the go-ahead for concrete pouring. It's wise to get this done as soon as possible (even the same day), especially in wet conditions that might cause your trench walls to collapse. Get your concrete company lined up ready for this. The inspector will not check you have everything square. If foundations are out of square there can be serious problems later as you won't be able to set out your walls how they should be. I always advise novice builders to go for wider trenches to give them that slight flexibility later. OK, it costs more in digging and concrete but it's cheaper to do this than to find your external walls running too near the concrete edge, or even off it! A good builder should, in contrast, get this right by measuring carefully and triangulating every corner to ensure squareness. This said, I always check trenches for dimensions, level and square myself, even when using a good builder.

I've detected all kinds of interesting things on watching how the inspector deals with key personnel

The final thing to check before passing your foundations will be to ensure that the reinforcing steel mesh is in place and properly placed. This is not usually used in deep-fill, strip foundations but can be vital in shallow ones. It should be tied with steel wires so all the individual pieces are linked together to form a 'mat'. The whole mesh should be propped up off the base of the trench so there's at least 50mm of concrete underneath it once the pour has been done. The mesh can't do its job lying on the floor of the trench.

Foundation concrete: Many inspectors will want to come when the concrete pour is actually being done. Now they check for mix quality and that the concrete is being placed properly (vibrated to exclude air pockets, no contamination from soil or other debris, and so on). Usually, if you've specified the correct concrete type from a ready-mix company there'll be no problems with the quality of the mix.

Concrete floor slab: Here the inspector will want to be sure there's no rubbish, vegetation and so on present before you install your damp-proof membrane and pour the concrete. They'll also check that this latter is installed in a way that ensures it can do its job of preventing water from getting into the slab. You get a one-shot chance at doing this. Once this membrane is down perforated it'll be trapped under concrete for ever yet not doing its job. Again, this is a stage I personally check, no matter how good my builder.

In certain areas (largely where granite is present) you may be required to have a radon barrier. This membrane goes in at floor slab time and keeps radon gas from entering the house through the floor. Talk to your designer about this.

It is almost universal to use steel mesh in a floor slab. Be guided by the comments above about steel in the foundations.

Damp-proof course: At the base of your building above the foundations there'll need to be a membrane of some kind that prevents water from the soil creeping up the walls. This is the damp-proof course. Your brick or block layers will have brought the foundation up to damp-proof level. The inspector will check that this is correctly placed at the right height above the finished ground level, and that it is continuous all around the perimeter of the building.

Drainage: When checking foul water drains (the ones from your lavatories and domestic machines) your inspector will look to see that: the runs have been sensibly planned; that the falls are sufficient to allow waste to drain under gravity in the desired directions; that there are rodding points (and probably inspection chambers) at all changes in direction and anywhere else that's necessary; and that all the joints have been properly fitted. More complex drainage systems need to be checked in other ways too. Your inspector may also want to do a leakage test. Here the system is sealed and a pressure gauge applied. There should be no meaningful fall in pressure over a fixed period of time. If there is, there's probably a bad joint or even a faulty pipe somewhere. This must be found and remedied before the drains are covered over. The drainage pipes should be laid in, and covered over with, ample pea shingle to protect them before covering with soil.

Roof completion: The main checks here are for structural strength. Whether you've built a cut roof or made one from trusses, the inspector will want to see that everything is properly braced (against wind loads) and that the rafter feet are properly fixed to the wall plate or block work at the perimeter walls.

Build complete: Each inspector has their own checklist here but expect them to be looking at: insulation; smoke detectors; methods of fire-escape, especially from bedrooms and second floors; and ventilation, especially to boiler rooms, kitchens and bathrooms. In theory they should check everything governed by the

Don't let the paperwork get you down

legislation (see the Parts outlined on page 64). How much of this is checked in how much detail by any individual inspector is up to them. I know a builder who made a mistake on a whole development of houses, in that his downstairs cloakrooms weren't compliant with the regs for disabled access. This was missed by the inspector but was later discovered by disgruntled homeowners. Of course it wasn't possible to rebuild a whole estate of houses to remedy this fault.

In general, you'll be able to rely on your designer to keep you on the good side of the regs. Certain suppliers and trades (windows and electrics are two examples) police themselves. This really only leaves a few Parts of the building regs that could be of concern to you as you plan your home.

In general, regulations are increasing year-on-year to make homes more energy efficient

The energy-efficiency element of your build will, in the very near future, undergo considerable changes in legislation. In general, regulations are increasing year-on-year to make homes more energy efficient. The various details of this differ from country to country, so I won't go into them here. Talk to your designer or building regs people for the latest news on all this.

Suffice it to say that as part L gets more demanding it makes sense to:

Up your game. If in doubt, do more rather than less. As buyers get more picky about energy ratings you could find this makes all the difference between getting a buyer and being unable to sell in a difficult market.

Avoid designs that include 'energy-losing hazard' features. Dormer and bay windows are classic examples.

Future-proof whenever you can. I know it can be hard but think ahead and listen to the pros on how these areas are likely to get tougher. Work on the assumption that things *will* definitely get tougher.

Good design will usually ensure you're well in the clear on all this. Brick, or other masonry, cavity walls can be built using heat-conserving blocks; cavity walls must have a 90mm panel of insulation within the cavity; timber frame houses can easily match the legal requirements with their 140mm stud depths; and roof insulation can easily be as deep as

Part M deals with disabled access:

- All changes in level, be they internal or external, must be made by slopes rather than steps
- There must be a solid path from your boundary to the front door
- A ramp up to your front door must be at least 900mm wide
- All internal doors must have a minimum clear opening of 750mm (front door 775mm)
- All new homes must have a downstairs cloakroom big enough to get a wheelchair into and turn
- Electrical sockets and light switches must be reachable from a wheelchair. This means all such installations must be between 450mm and 1200mm above finished floor level

Part L deals with energy conservation:

Five major areas are governed by Part L:

- Lighting must not use unnecessarily large amounts of energy
- Fuel and power must be conserved within the building
- The 'envelope' (outer skin) of the building must conserve heat
- Hot water and central heating systems must have controls
- Heat loss from water tanks and central heating must be minimised

250mm. Heat loss from windows and doors is regulated by their manufacturers; boilers and their control systems are also made to comply and even water saving is now encouraged, with low-flush and dual-flush toilets.

Some useful websites on building regs include:

www.safety.odpm.gov.uk/bregs/building.htm
www.hunter-jones.freeserve.co.uk
www.tso.co.uk/bookshop (the Stationery Office website to buy copies of the Regs)

Part B deals with Fire protection.

Some key issues here include:

- Each habitable room must have a suitably-sized window which can be opened as an escape in case of fire
- There must be a sufficient number of mains-operated smoke (or heat) detectors
- Your escape route to a main exit door must be no greater than a certain distance
- Your escape from a loft conversion (special rules apply)
- How the space is divided up (affects how smoke and fire can spread)
- The fire-resistance of various materials (especially of internal doors)

Permitted Development

What constitutes 'permitted development' differs in each part of the UK and the Republic of Ireland; seek local advice. As I wrote this book in late 2008, the rules governing permitted development changed dramatically.

Between 1997 and 2007 the numbers of domestic planning applications doubled to 330,000. The new rules will remove approximately 80,000 households a year from the planning system – about a quarter of the total number. By taking so many planning applications out of the system, local authorities will be less heavily burdened and more able to cope on larger, more complex planning applications. Hopefully, this will mean that local planning officers will be able to give a better service. The new measures will also save the nation up to £50 million each year.

The changes will allow some people to build both up and out without obtaining specific planning permission – which previously often cost as much as £1,000. They will also make it easier if you want to improve rather than move at a time like this when the property market is so difficult.

Rear extensions and loft conversions

Terraced: loft conversions can be up to 20 centimetres back from the eaves or have a maximum volume of 40 cubic metres. Also, a single- or two-storey rear extension can go back a maximum of 3 metres from the original house.

Semi-detached: loft conversions can be up to 20 centimetres back from the eaves and have a maximum volume of 50 cubic metres. In addition, a single- or two-storey rear extension can go back a maximum of 3 metres from the original house.

Detached: loft conversions can be up to 20 centimetres back from the eaves of the roof or have a maximum volume of 50 cubic metres. In addition, a rear extension can either be a single storey going 4 metres back from the original house, or a two-storey one going 3 metres back.

Ground floor rear extensions in conservation areas will be permitted (but loft conversions in such areas will continue to be restricted).

Driveways and parking areas

New driveways or parking areas over 5 square metres will not require planning permission if made from surfaces that allow water to soak through. A new user-friendly guide for builders and DIY-ers is available at:

www.communities.gov.uk/publications/planningandbuilding/pavingfrontgardens

Part of all these changes is a new section of the planning portal website (www.planningportal.gov.uk/uploads/hhg/houseguide.html). This is an interactive guide that helps the public understand planning requirements when making home improvements. You can click on the part of the house you want to change and it explains the rules.

Changes to the rules also mean that homeowners can install solar panels without planning permission.

Building regulations still apply to conversions and extensions even if they don't need planning permission under the new permitted development rules. And local councils will still have discretion to vary the planning rules. Given that household planning applications can be contentious – people will always be concerned about privacy, overlooking and loss of amenity – it will still be possible to involve the planners to ensure fair play for all.

Welcome though these changes are, it might have been even better to have given local authorities flexibility to set their own permitted development rights because they understand their unique housing and environmental situations best.

8 Money matters

I've looked on page 22 at how to fund your project and how to work out preliminary costs but now we'll look at how you should manage your finances on a regular basis.

Managing cash flow

There are eleven stages (see panel) in the average domestic build and each costs about the same proportion of the build. Knowing this, and talking things through with your builder, will allow you to plan your cash flow. This is important because, unless you are very wealthy, you won't have money sitting around waiting to be spent. Lenders tend to release money only once each stage of the build is complete (and signed off by a professional). In reality, therefore, your builder underwrites the cost of each stage until you get the cash and he, in turn, gets paid.

Try to build as fast as you can, as this minimises cash flow problems. People are usually happy to wait a couple of weeks to be paid but not a couple of months. In general, the building trade works best when paid quickly. Builders most like working for customers who pay on time, which is understandable because it is they who are at financial risk until they get paid. This is a huge gamble for many small builders as so many people find excuses not to pay them, especially at the end of the job.

One of the reasons clients find builders difficult is that builders are very often worried about money, contrary to popular belief. When things are getting difficult between you, for whatever reason, try to think how you'd feel if you couldn't be sure you'd be paid at the

There are several well-recognised stages to constructing a simple house:

- Groundworks: including site preparation, access road, foundations, drainage and main underground service supplies, and ground floor slab
- Ground floor walls (external and internal masonry ones), first floor structure
- Scaffolding, first floor walls, roof structure, chimneys
- Covering the roof
- Installing all windows and external doors (makes the place water-tight)
- Studwork internal walls, rainwater goods, soffits and fascias
- Plumbing and electrics, first fix
- Plastering/screeding and second fix carpentry
- Second fix electrics, fitting kitchen and cupboards
- Second fix plumbing, heating, finishing/decorating/tiling
- Snagging and external works

end of each month at your work. Every time a builder takes on a new, small client (such as you building your one-off home) he's taking a calculated risk. In the selection process before going to contract he'll be interviewing you as a potential employer every bit as much as you are assessing him!

Contingencies

If anyone tells you not to worry about a contingency sum, ignore them. This sum, usually about ten to fifteen per cent of the average-build cost, must be factored in right from the start, and included in your budget or you'll get into serious trouble. No job I have ever known has come in at the exact predicted price (unless it was ridiculously over-priced in the first place, or a pre-planned kit house). Similarly, no job I have ever dealt with has been built exactly as planned. Many things, some out of your control, such as the weather holding you up, can contribute to a larger spend than anticipated. Unless you have this amount of 'fat' in your budget, you'll be scrabbling around at the end worrying about how to pay the final stage payment to the builder. This can be extremely stressful and can quickly take the pleasure out of the whole adventure.

The contingency sum isn't there to be spent on a 'sexier' bathroom, or whatever. It is to be kept for when it's really needed. And it will be!

All builds have an intrinsic risk factor that needs to be taken into account when planning your contingency. Here are some guidelines of what sort of contingency to allow:

Small extension	10%
Large extension	15%
New house build	20%
Major renovation/ conversion	30%
Period restoration	40% ++
You building a new house, on your own, hands-on, for the first time	50%

Keeping financial records

There's little point making great financial plans if you don't keep a watchful eye on expenditure as things progress. This seems a chore at the time but it's essential. Keep a daily site diary (see page 158) of everything significant that happens and a separate financial Day Book which tracks all transactions involving money. Never throw any piece of paper away! Keep all delivery dockets, receipts, invoices, cheque stubs, bank statements, and so on so you can account for every penny spent, especially cash payments that can mount up and may not be easily accounted for. This will be especially important if you are intending to claim back VAT on the build. You get only one chance to claim back your VAT (at the end of the job) and if you don't have everything in place then, you'll simply lose loads of money unnecessarily.

One way of making financial control easier for yourself is to have an account with a local builders' merchant. Not only will you get a trade discount (though not as good a deal as their bigger customers), their monthly statement is clear and there are a lot of billing odds and ends under one roof, so to speak. Striking the right deal with a good merchant should be one of your early tasks, well before building begins (see page 168 for how to do this).

If you are computer-literate, keep a spreadsheet and up-date it at least once a week. There will always be changes to your planned build and thus to the budget. These usually come at groundwork stage and can be very costly. Changing a foundation detail, for example, can suddenly add thousands to even well-planned costings. If you can't run to a spreadsheet your financial Day Book will help keep tabs on how cash flow is going.

Before sanctioning any changes, be sure to have full agreed prices in writing from the parties concerned.

All this financial watchfulness is important so things don't run out of control before you realise it. It's all too easy to make small changes here and there which, at the time, appear trivial in the context of the whole budget but which cumulatively come back to bite you at a later date.

Warranties and insurance

Warranties

A structural warranty is rather like a guarantee for your new build. It is a certificate that says your work has been done properly, to the best recognised standards. It will also cover you for a restricted menu of faults that might occur over a fixed period of years. This is really like an insurance policy in that you pay for it and hope not to have to claim in subsequent years! It's good to have, though, not just for your own peace of mind but in case you want to sell at some stage. Because the work will have been inspected at intervals by someone on behalf of the warranty company, this gives comfort to any future buyer. There's often concern among people buying from self-builders as they can't know whether things have been done properly. Your architect could give you a final sign-off document to say he inspected everything along the way and all is well. But this will, of course, cost money. His professional indemnity will cover him only for as long as he pays the premiums, though. If this runs out, for whatever reason, you could find yourself without cover. And, professional cover like this rarely lasts for ten years – which is the time you could expect from a structural warranty cover from one of the household-name providers.

A structural warranty usually covers:

- Reimbursement for repairs to the structure that are needed within the period of the warranty. There may be a ceiling on this amount. Clarify this at the time you take out the policy
- A guarantee that your builder will put right anything (covered by the policy, or his own policy) within two years of completing your build
- Financial protection if your builder goes bust

A warranty is good to have, not just for your own peace of mind but in case you want to sell at some stage

It's also possible, for an extra premium, to cover self-building or self-managed projects with a warranty. Some companies will pay out if you discover pollution or toxic materials that would cost a lot to clean up. As these warranties are, by definition, insuring you against long-term risks, go with a large company that you have reason to believe will still be around in ten years!

Don't imagine that because the Building Control Inspector has done his job this will be of any use to you in this context. It won't. They don't inspect to provide you with a guarantee for the future. If you want this, you'll have to pay for a warranty.

Insurance

The complexity of the insurance on your self-build will surprise and probably horrify you. Whatever your emotional response, don't skimp on it. We live in a highly litigious society today where everyone sues everyone else at the drop of a hat – and things are getting worse. You simply cannot afford to be uninsured – especially as construction remains one of the most dangerous industries.

Check that your policy covers exactly what you need. Get several quotes, as with any insurance and be sure you are comparing apples with apples. Risks to be covered include public liability insurance, employer's liability insurance and actual site cover.

Lender, builder and client...the eternal triangle

Public liability insurance covers you against the risk that a member of the public, whether working on or visiting the site, suffers an injury or dies. This should also cover you against other people's property getting damaged. For example a truck leaves your site, splattering mud all over the road. Someone skids on this and kills a passing child. Or one of your concrete trucks demolishes your neighbour's wall. If you employ a main contractor he should have this type of policy in place himself. Make sure you see all the paperwork to be sure it's up to date. I have had people mislead me about their insurance cover. Frankly, I still like to have my own cover irrespective of what the builder has, just to be safe.

Employer's liability insurance is important even when you are building yourself. From an income tax point of view you are not the technical employer of self-employed sub-contractors but you are responsible for them from an insurance point of view.

Site cover provides protection for things on the site. Unfortunately, many sites have problems with theft of materials and plant, so it makes sense to have everything well insured. Such a policy should cover materials, vandalism, damage caused by adverse weather, fire damage and accidental damage (for example your loader backs into the just-completed conservatory!). You may find some insurance companies require site security. This could mean having fencing all round, lighting, or even security cameras. I have had meaningful plant disappear from a highly visible site. The theft of high-cost kitchen appliances, sanitary and finishing materials can blow your budget out of the water if you aren't insured.

Other things I like to insure include existing buildings. I've done a lot of re-furbs. The value of such a place is in the planning permission that comes with the rotten old building. The actual bricks and mortar are worth very little. But if anything were to happen to this structure, the project could be lost as the planning permission would die with the building.

Most energy-saving innovations have a long pay-back time, often running beyond ten years

It's also worth getting personal injury cover for you. If you were to have an accident the knock-on costs could be massive, given that you are pivotal to the whole process. Some people also take out legal insurance cover, though I never have. This covers you in the event of protracted legal disputes that would soon make nonsense of your building budget.

If you have a temporary home (a caravan or mobile home) on the site, don't forget this too will need to be insured.

Insurance claims for damaged done to your home through fire, flood or other structural damage

Every home should be insured and if you have cause to claim on your insurance you must be aware of your rights:

- You are entitled to 'like for like' replacement
- A Loss Adjuster is employed by the insurer to get the repair done satisfactorily at the most economic cost

However, you can insist on who you want to work on your home, provided you have confidence in your ability to choose. You do not have to have the cheapest quotation contracted for the work.

Loss Adjusters employed by the insurers will conduct supervision, however if there is a large amount of work I would strongly advise you to take steps to independently employ a professional, whether it be an architect, a quantity surveyor or building supervisor.

Spending to save

I'm mentioning this because it's a subject I personally find difficult. Mass market developers never spend a penny they can't justify on commercial grounds. But we self-builders are different. If we're intending to live in the place for some years (and almost all my clients tell me it'll be for ever) then we can take a view about such expensive capital items as solar panels, geo-thermal heating, or high-quality external materials that need virtually no maintenance.

The problem is that many of these things are very nice to have and can start producing savings or advantages from day one. But truth be told, most have a long pay-back time, often running beyond ten years. Unless you are certain you'll be living in your new-build for many years I suggest you take a commercial developer's view and ask yourself how such items will add value when you come to sell in the future.

If your budget will stretch to it at the time of the build, then go ahead. If not, put the subject to one side and don't re-visit it in the future with any 'if onlys'!

9 What builders are and how they work

Before going any further with how to manage your project I'll share some insights into the building industry, how it works, and what builders actually do.

Most people, on a day-to-day basis, refer to 'builders' as if everyone in the construction and building industries were the same. This is not the case.

Starting at the top of the tree are the major, often multinational, publicly-quoted companies that take on huge projects in both the public and private sectors. They can cope equally well with a hydro-electric dam in India and a development of 200 houses in Birmingham. These huge builders are really in a world of their own. They work in an industry called construction which, although roughly similar to your project, is on such a vast scale, and involves so many more rules and regulations it is effectively another world from ordinary building. These companies employ very skilled people at professional and management levels who can think their way around unique problems involving millions of pounds, and can often do so very quickly. This is usually because they have substantial resources to call upon in the shape of in-house and consulting professionals.

Such companies are best known as 'constructors' rather than builders. Of course they need plumbers and plasterers like you and I do on our smaller builds but they also rely heavily on trades and skills almost never seen in domestic building work. The fun thing here is that all kinds of technologies previously only used in the commercial construction world are now becoming practical in domestic building projects. I frequently attend trade construction shows and usually bring back something that can be used in a domestic setting. An example is the use of curtain walling, usually only to be found as the outer skin of an office block, as part of a glass-walled house.

But all this said, the world of construction remains on a different plane from that of normal builds. For example, when you cost out your house you'll spend about a third to a half of your total budget on your land and the rest on the build. Of the build cost itself about forty to fifty per cent will be on materials and the rest on labour.

However, when a major construction company becomes involved in a new shopping centre, for example, the sums are roughly equal quarters for: the land; the build; borrowing the money; and.....architects' and other professional fees. In other words a large property developer might spend only one quarter of his multi-million budget on the actual building itself. And next time you moan about what your architect charges, just bear these figures in mind!

Now to builders the public deal with. These can vary from a one-man band who multi-tasks and is competent at several trades, to a fair-sized company (main contractor) that employs its own men directly and sub-contracts out the rest of the work, often to tried-and-tested 'subbies' (see page 85) they use time and again who don't want to be employed full-time by one builder. The one-man band can be very good indeed but what you see is what you get. There are obvious dangers of putting all your eggs in one small basket, though it can work for small projects.

A fair-sized building company can come in cheaper and faster than a man-and-a-van outfit

The larger building contractor, however, has in-house management, a pricing department, even perhaps their own engineer or designer, and so on. They'll work confidently on several projects at once and shift men and plant around to get the best use from them. This can sometimes mean that a fair-sized building company can come in cheaper and faster than a man-and-a-van outfit, even though the former has larger overheads. This has just happened to me....the largest contractor came in with the lowest price.

How builders work

Building is a highly risky business. When you seek out a builder for your build you'll, of course, interview him. But, more to the point, he'll be wary of you. The problem with small, private building projects is that the builder cannot know with any certainty if and when you're going to pay him. Given that every new build, major conversion or extension is a one-off and that the builder won't know you from Adam, how can he be sure you'll actually pay?

This concern is especially valid when the facts are that a substantial proportion of customers try not pay their builders their final instalment, or if they do so, delay it for as long as possible. And then there are those people who find they cannot pay, for reasons beyond their control. The average building company has scores of such tales of woe and is only too aware that their competitors are going bust around them

You usually *can* judge a book by its cover

in numbers that would shock any other industry.

A TV shop wouldn't dream of letting you out of the door unless you had paid, or could prove you'll pay later. And this is for a few hundred pounds. Imagine, then, how financially exposed a builder is when pitching for your job.

It is the domestic building industry norm for builders to be paid in stages and in arrears. This means your builder is financing your build until you pay him. I'll bet you can't name many industries where this occurs, especially with customers they don't know. Your builder is thus giving you unsecured credit, which you'd have difficulty getting even from your own bank. True, he'll be getting credit for a while from his suppliers but his workforce won't wait to be paid and his fixed overheads will rumble on.

> **Your builder is financing your build until you pay him**

All this means that building companies feel vulnerable a lot of time and try to cope with this by: pricing accordingly; being canny about which customers they take on; insisting they do no further work until agreed stage payments have been made; and using various other ruses I'll come to.

As far as most builders are concerned, a good customer is one who pays. An unfair trick that some self-builders play is to keep their money tied up, in the name of good financial husbandry, in some sort of savings account until it's required. The builder then has to wait for 30 days, or even longer, for this cash to become available. In the meantime he is out of pocket, which costs him money. This is obviously not the way to get a builder to work for you again.

Another horror for a builder is the client who never really had all the cash in the first place, or who has over-run because of changes to the specification and now has no cash to pay the final bill. Some such unscrupulous clients now find fault with the build, list vast numbers of snags, and so on....anything to delay the moment they'll have to pay. Sometimes this is a sort of punishment, conscious or unconscious, of the builder they feel has treated them badly. But it's not fair. It's vital to keep a keen eye on your funds at all stages so your builder doesn't find himself bank-rolling your inefficiencies.

In my experience it's always best to come clean with a builder about money. If your financial circumstances change, or you over-run your budget by adding loads of extras, say so, and see what can be done. You'd be furious if your boss told you at the end of the month that you'd have to wait a few weeks for your salary cheque....or that it might not even come at all.

How builders make money

First off, they try to avoid taking on customers who won't pay!

The next thing I want to say is that it isn't that easy making a profit from domestic building. Everyone teases builders about how rich they are but, truth be told, there are far easier and less risky ways of making money.

> **Many consumer magazines fail to take into account the substantial fixed overhead you too will have, just as your builder does**

If you use a builder for your work (see below) it'll definitely cost you more than doing it yourself. It is generally said that you can save about 25% of the build cost by going this route. But this figure needs looking at very carefully. All builders have fixed overheads that include phone bills; vehicles to run; book-keeping, accountancy and legal fees; insurances; office rents and so on. On top of this your builder will actually be managing the build itself.

These two sets of contractor's expenses (fixed overheads plus the management work he personally does) can easily add 15 to 20 per cent to the base costs of materials, labour and so on, before he even starts to make a trading profit. This real profit can come from various sources:

- Pricing the work high so that, if he gets it, he makes a serious profit (maybe up to 50%, including the above 20%). Many builders do this because they know they can't rely on pricing accurately enough, and so could lose money. The public demands a fixed-price contract so they know where they stand financially but then expects their builder to swallow all kinds of extra costs, which, of course he cannot do. One reason you'll get such different fixed-priced quotes on your job when you put it out to tender is that every builder is in a particular financial and workload position at any one time and has to assess the risk and desirability of your work at that moment in his business life. Catch him a month later and the situation could have changed completely

- Charge a lot for 'extras'. This is the oldest ruse in the builder's book. Many a contractor charges competitively to get the work, then marks up extras heavily to make his real profit. A canny builder may, for example, look at your plans and your thinking, see you haven't specified things properly and rub his hands as he knows that within a few months you'll be begging him to do extra work for lots of money. This is one reason for having a water-tight specification (see page 51)

- Marking up materials he supplies. He might, for example, charge you X for a specialist type of window but negotiate up to a 30% discount from his supplier, only some of which he'll pass on to you

- Pricing it high if he's not convinced about your ability to pay or thinks the job will be problematic. This is really a sort of insurance....and perfectly justifiable. It's his gamble

- 'Covering'. This is an informal process in which busy local builders who know one another get together in a sort of cartel to decide which will get a particular job. This is especially common in smaller towns and cities where there are only a few good-quality, medium-sized builders that do most of the good work. In this system even the lowest quote is, in effect, a high one, so the builder who gets it still makes a good profit. The others simply didn't want the job anyway. Their chance will come next time. This all comes about because we expect builders to quote for free. In reality, as I know, it costs a lot of money to prepare a quote. We often employ a quantity surveyor to do quotes, at considerable expense. By the nature of things only one in four or five of all quotes results in work, but this overhead has to be paid for somehow. Covering helps offset this cost. As this book goes to press a scandal has come to light in the UK involving huge building corporations in covering operations. It is likely that the law will now be tightened on this murky subject as it has involved vast sums of public money.

The public demands a fixed-price contract

You, of course, will be managing the project as a whole, of which the build is the biggest fraction. But even if you manage your own build, this will still cost you. I look at this more below. Suffice it to say that you will not save 25% by managing the whole build yourself and cutting out the main contractor. Many consumer magazines give the impression that you will but they fail to take into account the substantial fixed overhead you too will have, just as your builder does. It also assumes that your personal time is worth nothing.

A way round the whole profit scenario is to do a deal with your builder in which he is guaranteed a profit margin of, say 15%, based on his opening up his books to show you what in real terms everything has cost. This is very fair and I like to use it. It works especially well if you personally manage everything well, work hand-in-glove with your builder and keep on top of costs. In effect your builder becomes a partner in the build. Some builders are reluctant to do this, though, because they can make far better profits by other methods.

Why bother with a builder?

The world of domestic building has a very poor press. Most people's opinions of builders comes somewhere between those on politicians and estate agents!

None of this is helped by the nature of the building cycle which is characterised by dramatic ups and downs, following national and even international financial cycles

Many people distrust builders to have their client's best interests at heart and there's a huge amount of suspicion around. None of this is helped by the nature of the building cycle which is characterised by dramatic ups and downs, following national and even international financial cycles. When times are buoyant all kinds of slapdash cowboys enter the market to mop up the flood of work that's available. Many of these shouldn't be in the trade at all, and once the boom is over, they disappear. During this phase professional, capable building companies find themselves overwhelmed with work, can't obtain enough good-quality workmen and thus get a bad name for maybe not even wanting to quote, and when they do, for ripping people off, when, in fact, they're simply making hay while the sun shines.

Having seen both sides of this coin over thirty years I have to say most stereotypes of builders are largely unwarranted. It's true that cowboy outfits exist but overall, the average small-to-medium-sized contractor and most subbies are honest, decent people trying to do their best and run a good business. I have experience of many different industries and can't say that building is intrinsically any worse than any other.

This said, given that you want to do a major build, what are your alternatives?

You will spend huge amounts of time and energy communicating with your contractor, managing him, and making a million decisions as the job progresses

There are five ways you could get the work done. The method you choose will affect what it costs but many of the so-called 'savings' by going the various routes can cost you more in hidden ways. It's vital to be honest with yourself about all this. It's all too easy to kid ourselves we are saving fortunes by not using a builder but this may not be the case when we factor everything in. Most people who claim to have 'built their own house' in fact have not done so. The overwhelming majority have had it built for them by a builder, with them providing varying amounts of input.

Using a main contractor. This is the simplest and the one most 'self-builders' opt for. The contractor will, of course, expect to make a profit on the job. This will be anything from 15 to 25 per cent but can be very much higher. He'll manage the build, buy the materials, hire sub-contractors and so on. Just because you take this route, don't for a moment think your work is done. It won't be. You will still spend huge amounts of time and energy communicating with your contractor, managing him, and making a million decisions as the job progresses. This is the easiest route to go but it is not easy!

Using a project manager. Project managers work in many different ways and offer very different levels of service. Many have no formal qualifications but most come from the building industry, possibly with an HNC in building studies. It's perfectly reasonable to ask for details of their background and about recent jobs they've worked on. There are some around who specialise in self-builds. Go on the Web and also look at www.apm.org.uk

Project managers are usually very flexible and can offer a host of services tailored to your needs. They can price the project from a bill of quantities drawn up by a quantity surveyor; find a builder and/or various sub-contractors; supervise the project on an almost daily basis; buy materials, fixtures and fittings; and even hire people and run the site as a hands-on manager. All I can say is that if you choose this route be very clear exactly what you're getting for your money. It can take a lot off your mind and can save you about ten per cent compared with a main contractor, even allowing for the project manager's fees (which could be about ten per cent of the build budget).

A good project manager can also deal with legal contracts and ensure that Health and Safety regs are complied with. He'll also be able to supply you with a 'critical path analysis' of your job and set everything up ready for you to project manage, if you want.

If you are working full-time yet need someone to interface between you and the contractors, this is the way to go. Some companies, especially loft converters, kitchen installers, and large building companies all have their own staff project managers. They'll appoint one to supervise your job. He will be your point of reference with the company.

Manage the whole build yourself. This is, in reality, a route chosen only by the dedicated few who can afford to take a very long time off work, who are retired or unemployed, or who work seasonally. It is certainly the most rewarding but unless you've done it before, can be very harrowing. After all, you are learning, on the job, to be a main contractor. More to the point, you are in effect being a speculative builder....and one with very little, or no experience. In reality you'll be spending more than 2,000 hours working on something that may not turn out to be the winner you dreamed of.

All lessons in life come at a cost. Given that you'll be learning thousands of lessons on your first house or other major build, it'll be virtually impossible to assess what they will cost you. Obviously, the more of the hands-on work you do yourself, the bigger the savings you'll make. I reckon it's possible, by doing everything you reasonably can (except, say the electrics, and one or two other highly-specialist trades), to save about 40% on what a builder would charge. But this is the very, very best saving.....unachievable by all but the most highly-motivated and dedicated self-builder who'll end up living and breathing the project for the best part of two years. It's instructive to bear in mind that very few such

'8,641...8,642...8,643. That's the brickwork calculated. I'll show them why they need a QS!'

Some Dos and Don'ts when choosing a builder:

DO:

- Keep your eyes open as you go around the area where you intend to build. Look for developments that are similar to yours. Check the builder's site for helpful hints (see below). By choosing some-one who does work like yours you'll save yourself a lot of time asking inappropriate builders to quote
- Ask friends, family or workmates who they'd recommend
- Talk to people who've used your proposed contractor before. Ask how they got on with him and consider whether, knowing your own personality, you would find him equally good. Bear in mind during this discussion that things that would drive you mad may not have affected this other party in the same way. Ideally, talk to more than one customer
- Try to use a builder that belongs to a recognised trade body. Talk to the Federation of Master Builders (FMB); their website www.findabuilder.co.uk is also helpful. The National Federation of Builders is useful too. If someone says he's a member of a professional body, check this is actually the case
- Ensure that your proposed builder will give an insurance-backed warranty on his work (see page 74)
- Ask a local architect/designer/ engineer who they like to work with
- Insist on written, detailed quotations (see page 87)
- Insist on seeing their public liability insurance certificates

DON'T:

- Deal with anyone who refuses to give you references for previous work
- Get involved with 'cash-in-hand' deals
- Do anything that avoids paying VAT. If a builder has a very small outfit he may fall below the legal threshold for registering for VAT. If so, is he large enough to cope with your job? If this is not the case he could be in jail for defrauding the Customs and Excise rather than on your site!
- Accept jargon that appears confusing. If he flim-flams or patronises you now, just imagine how bad things could get in the future
- Go near a builder who thinks contracts are unnecessary
- Use anyone who tries to get your work by knocking the competition
- Ignore your feelings if you are suspicious or uneasy
- Go with a builder who has a mobile phone as his only point of contact
- Accept a really low quote
- Use anyone who can start very soon. No good builder sits around waiting for work
- Be tempted by a builder who thinks specifications are a waste of time because 'things work out on the job'
- Listen to any builder who wants you to pay in advance

devotees go on to become professional builders! Anyway, being good at one thing doesn't mean you'll be good at another.

At a less dedicated level, in return for your expensive mistakes and lots of stress, you might save up to 25% on what a main contractor would charge but it will take you much longer. Of course your own time doesn't come free. Neither do your nerves and energy. There's no such thing as a free lunch, after all. Unless you are really sure this is the route for you, I'd suggest keeping the day job and going routes 1 or 2, bearing in mind that both will still make huge demands on your time, emotions and energy.

This whole subject is easily obscured by self-delusion and wishful thinking. Many of the property TV shows trumpet the supposed substantial profits made by their subjects but rarely mention that in a rising market, had they bought the property and done nothing at all to it they would have made a good profit. All their hard work, worry and sleepless nights may have actually created little extra value.

Of course your own time doesn't come free. Neither do your nerves and energy. There's no such thing as a free lunch, after all

When deciding to self-build it's vital to know yourself very well; to listen to those who love and care about you; to be aware of your motives for doing it; and to be realistic about what else you'd be doing if you weren't doing this. Self-building for money alone can backfire badly.

Using a package company. Such companies offer fixed-price answers to your problems. They can handle everything from design to supplying labour and managing the complete build. But this comes at a price. Such a system is usually found in the timber frame industry. The main advantage (to be set against an otherwise high cost) is that the company's designers know their product inside out and will use tried-and-tested methods and build units to achieve a good result quite quickly. Such outfits are also very practical about linking your budget to what they can supply. This can be appealing to first-time self-builders as everything seems more certain than going the 'architect' route. In return for higher costs you'll get more financial certainty and a lot less grief.

Such outfits are also very practical about linking your budget to what they can supply

A mixture of all of the above. In this approach you could use a package company to supply and erect the house up to weather-tight; then employ yourself and your own subbies to do the rest. This way of doing things means you'll get a good head start with the main build, which gives the project great momentum, and you can then decide how much time and effort you can personally put in as time goes by. A disadvantage is that this way of working can leave gaps between stools down which everyone can fall! A good designer can help smooth all this out for you.

Lastly, a word about selective amnesia. Many's the woman who swears, during labour or immediately after giving birth, that she'll never go there again. Doctors then see this same woman, perhaps only a year or so later, happily looking forward to another birth! Self-builders are much like this. Once the job is done and the 'baby' 'born' they quickly forget the stresses and pains they endured. Their selective memory recalls only the good times and they seek out another project. Those close to them sometimes have to remind them just how hard it all was (sometimes more so on those around them). But, as with having more babies, they're immune to such warnings!

Choosing a builder

If you choose to employ a builder for your work, making the right choice could alter your life for the next year or more. This makes it a rather important decision. As the manager of your project this will be the most important decision you'll make. And given that you'll be legally responsible for the work, you'll need to be able to trust the builder you choose to perform his side of the contract professionally.

There's no substitute for going to see your proposed builder at work on a site like yours. When visiting his site, here's what to look for:

- How does the whole place feel, at first glance, even from across the street? Does it look professional, tidy and safe?
- How are cars and other vehicles parked? Are they annoying neighbours, or otherwise parked thoughtlessly? Is there evidence they've damaged the pavement, or other public areas?
- Does his van have a name, address and telephone number on it? Always a good sign
- Are there tracks of mud, thoughtlessly positioned skips, or building debris on the public road?
- Is there a name board displaying the contractor's details?
- Does the site look secure, with a fence where it adjoins the pavement?
- What do the men look like? Are they a scruffy lot, or professional-looking tradesmen? Is there a scattering of subbies' vehicles around, with suitable signage?
- Are there radios blaring?
- When you approach workers, are they helpful and polite?
- Do you find yourself tripping over trailing extension leads or other obstructions?
- Are materials neatly stacked, or just dumped around the site?
- Is there rubbish strewn around the place?
- Are workers doing dangerous jobs wearing protective gear?

An absence of any individual items on this list doesn't mean you should walk away but the greater the evidence of unprofessional conditions, the more wary you should be.

The UK Government's Trustmark Scheme helps the public avoid cowboy builders. Anyone displaying the logo can be trusted to come up to certain agreed basic standards. Their work is insured, or can be insured. Check on the internet to see if someone is on the Scheme.

Hiring sub-contractors (subbies)

In strict legal terms a subcontractor is someone who works for a main contractor. In everyday usage it means an individual tradesman or small group of tradesmen working together to supply a service. The minute you employ a subcontractor you become a main contractor. Technically, from a taxation point of view, this means you have to know what you're doing. Go to www.hmrc.gov.uk, choose Leaflets and Booklets, go to the Business section and search for CIS 340. This contains everything you'll need to know.

It's easy to lose sight of an important fact about subbies – they need managing by someone. This could be you, if you are managing your build; your builder if he's hired them; or your project manager, if you use one.

The best way to find a good subbie is to ask around, listening especially to local friends and family. People involved in building: builders' merchants; designers (yours especially, of course); quantity surveyors; building inspectors; planners; estate agents; and so on can all be good sources. As a very last resort, look in the Yellow Pages or the local paper. You may feel you need to take up references for key people (your plumber and electrician, for example) but might be prepared to take a leap of faith on others, given that you'll be able to end your contract with them at very short notice if they turn out to be a bad choice. If in doubt, always listen to your designer. Indeed, he may have a bank of

A basic rule of thumb when hiring subbies is:

- Use only people who come with a personal recommendation from someone you trust
- See some of their previous work, if possible. This can be hard to arrange but you can at least call someone they've recently worked for
- Try to get a price beforehand. Most 'proper businesses' such as electrical contractors and plumbers will happily do this but many other trades simply don't have the time or inclination to provide proper quotes
- Use people who belong to a professional or trade body if possible, though they'll probably cost more
- Use people who have been independently assessed, for example with NVQs
- Make sure your main subbies will provide a guarantee with their work
- Don't pay the complete amount before the work is done
- Don't work with subbies who'll give you price reductions for cash or to avoid VAT. Although you're not responsible for policing their tax affairs, it's a nuisance when the Revenue comes back to you on it. They might then take the opportunity to scrutinise *your* affairs, as such practices make *you* look dodgy!

tried-and-tested favourites he likes to use....or indeed, insists on using! This is one of the real advantages of using a local designer.

The national Self-Build and Renovation Centre in Swindon has a list of UK contractors and subcontractors.
See www.mykindofhome.co.uk

In reality, once you get into the thick of running your site you may well find yourself grateful for whom you can get, so all your best intentions could go by the board. I have built up a bank of trusted and reliable tradesmen over the years who like working on my projects but if you're doing a one-off build you won't have this luxury.

Subbies like to work in one of two ways. The first are labour-only. They work singly or in groups (usually of brickies, plasterers, roofers, block layers, or ground workers). You agree a going rate for their time and you supply everything else for them except, perhaps, specialised plant in the case of ground workers.

The second group of subbies is more sophisticated in that they price for both their time and the materials together. Many of these do proper quotes and run nice little businesses. A good example would be a plumbing/heating engineer. They'll expect to make something on the goods they supply, which will, obviously, add to the cost. Sometimes, though, I've found that such an outfit can source things more cheaply than I can and still come in at a good price even when marking things up. In a way you're asking such subbies to take a management load off your shoulders and this will cost you. Depending on how you manage your site (for example, you may still be holding down a full-time job), this could be a very acceptable cost. This approach is also good if you want to inject some certainty into your budgeting. If you're a novice builder you can only hope that a particular element will come out at what you think it will. Using what I call a 'small business subbie' could take the guesswork out of this and give you peace of mind, even if it is a bit more pricey.

One difficulty with hiring subbies is knowing whether to get them to price for the whole job or to employ them on a day-work basis with you supplying the materials and them taking as long as it takes. Given that most self-builders are hard up for cash it makes sense to get work priced rather than going for 'day work'. This gives the subbie an incentive to get the job done for the price he quotes but it's worth pointing out that if there's any doubt in his mind about future difficulties or aggravations he'll price the work accordingly and you'll kick yourself for not getting him to do the (what turns out to be smooth-running) job on a day rate. This is a real dilemma because obviously subbies are looking after themselves and leaving you to worry about your finances. They will not, and why should they, put themselves at financial risk on your job. This decision can often be a close call and will come down to your need for financial certainty at the start of that particular element of the work. You'll also find it very hard indeed, early on in your building career, to have any real notion of how much work any given subbie can do in a day. Even highly experienced builders can find that a specialist subbie turns up with some new piece of kit that will enable them to do the work in half the time. This happed to me with the installation of forty doors on one project. The carpenter arrived with a superb bench with special jigs for hinges, handles and locks that meant he fitted twice as many doors in a day than I'd ever seen done before!

I've sometimes found that such an outfit can source things more cheaply than I can and still come in at a good price even when marking things up

'Measured rates' are another source of grief. Even perfectly honest subbies can get measurements wrong off the drawings, sometimes by as much as ten per cent. Block workers and brickies usually 'measure through openings' as if the whole area was to be filled by them. On many of the properties I build, there are huge voids for large windows. This makes masonry quotes seem high. Things may not be as bad as they appear, though, as some such trades will often fit the window frames as they go and may also have to fiddle with reveals, damp-proofing details, insulation, and cavity trays.

Managing subbies is a bit of an art form. Many of them will be on your site for a very short time as hired guns to get a job done. Others (especially electricians, plumbers, kitchen/

Some subbies will become real allies in your whole project and contribute enthusiastically and creatively, given a chance

bedroom/bathroom fitters and second-fix chippies) will become real allies in your whole project and contribute enthusiastically and creatively, given a chance. The first group will, by and large, be happy to do a good job and get a fair day's pay whilst the second group will want to be more involved and will, on average, be more business-like and intelligent. I regularly use plumbers and electricians who earn as much as a doctor, and their contribution is well worth it.

Estimates, quotations and contracts

Once you've decided on using a builder you'll need to get some prices. There are several ways of achieving this.

Quantity surveyor (QS). This professional will take your drawings and specification and create a Bill of Quantities and Materials Schedule. For a modest fee you'll get an accurate list and cost of everything you'll need, for each stage of your project. He'll also put a time schedule against all this. In order to get this really accurate you may have to spend quite a bit of time with your QS.

Estimating computer software. This route puts more responsibility on to you and costs only a few hundred pounds but is accurate, provided you input the correct information. EasyPrice Pro, Fast Estimate, and HBXL's Estimator and Project Manager are all worth looking at. Such systems can, however, soon get out of date and are costly to update. They're probably only useful if you're doing several projects. If you are confident and experienced, this can be the route to choose but it means losing out on the experience of a pro who could come up with creative ideas and/or save you money and stress.

Some designers offer a pricing service but their time is often too expensive to use like this.

Estimates and quotes (quotations)

Estimates and quotes are not the same, so it's vital to be sure what you are reading when you receive one.

An estimate is a statement of expectation of the cost of a project or individual task. Estimates are done where there's a degree of uncertainty about the nature, materials, quality or scope of the task. This is very common in refurbishment and renovation work where it can be near-impossible to gain sufficient access to the structure. It's also difficult before diagnostic demolition to know what you're dealing with. With the best will in the world your contractor cannot be psychic and can therefore only give an intelligent guess (estimate) at what might be involved.

Problems also occur where there's unforeseen difficult ground, unexpected woodworm or other infestations, impossible-to-diagnose structural issues, and so on.

It's vital, therefore, to look carefully at estimates and to get your contractor to tell you what the worst-case scenario could be, from his experience. You really need to be prepared for the worst outcome because if you can't cope with this financially, the whole project could grind to a halt.

If necessary, get two professional inputs on such matters as your contractor may want to minimize the financial hazards, so he can get the work and then charge all this as extras.

The gentleman's agreement

When agreeing in advance on additional work, be sure to pin down exact rates per man per hour or day; square metre rates; materials costs and so on. Also ask about any possible plant costs that could hike the price.

On reading your estimate it's wise to allow at least 10% extra for contingencies and if working with old buildings or refurbs, 40% or more.

Once you agree to an estimate be sure that all extra work is sanctioned by you (ideally in writing) before it's actually done. Your designer, or other professional, will help monitor this work so you are charged only for what is actually necessary and completed. Keep lots of photos of this extra work, especially if it's going to be hidden.

A quotation (quote) or tender is a binding undertaking to provide a service or material and is valid for a stated period of time.

Seeking tenders

Whether you are going to use a main contractor or a team of subbies it's vital to send the same drawings and spec to all parties or you'll never be able to compare their prices. Send everything to three or four comparable parties. This should mean you'll end up with one or two comparable tenders. Beware that

When sending documents out to tender you should make it clear that:

- The party that comes in with the cheapest price will not necessarily win the contract
- You want their quotation back by a particular date (say three weeks from the day they receive it). You may have to chase by phone. An efficient, timely response speaks well of a contractor
- Only the work as described should be quoted for. If the contractor cannot, for some reason, quote for certain items, he should give reasons why
- If the builder doesn't want to quote at all he should say so as soon as possible (so you can go to someone else)
- Those tendering should seek clarification if in any doubt
- If the contractor finds errors or inconsistencies in the design or spec he should notify you at once
- You will need to see a programme of works along with the tender
- You want your contribution to the process taken into account
- If the contractor intends to substitute products or methods he should say so now
- You want to hear how the contractor will ensure quality control, including how the build (and sub-contractors) will be managed
- You need to be satisfied how he will manage health and safety issues
- You will not pay for the preparation of the tender
- You want to retain all salvaged materials to sell on yourself (unless you agree otherwise)
- You will need regular progress reports and site meetings (at intervals to be agreed in writing)
- You will want a cash flow forecast
- Day-work agreements must be agreed at this stage
- You expect the contractor to make good the area (in ways to be agreed) on completion of the work and that this is done at his expense.
- He will take control of waste management and deal with it according to the law
- He will set daily working-time limits and not cause nuisance with smoke, dust, vermin, fumes, noise, and anything else that's important on your site
- He will not burn materials on site
- He will read meters at the start and end of the project and be responsible for paying the bills

When you receive a tender, check:

- You are comparing like with like. Sometimes a good builder will, for example, insert something you've forgotten. Others might 'miss' this item and hope to get a premium out of you later
- The acceptance validity period suits you. Most quotes are valid for between four and 12 weeks. Try to insist on 12 weeks
- The items on the tender match those on the bill of quantities
- All the work has been priced for, not just those items the contractor is prepared to undertake
- It is not too cheap. Some builders price competitively to get the work and discover later that they've left themselves in a difficult position. They now start to cut corners on quality or materials, or even have to abort the whole project. This is a dangerous situation to find yourself in because any incoming contractor will know you are in a spot and charge accordingly. Electrical or plumbing work carried out by the first contractor may not be deemed acceptable by your new contractor who could (given he has to stand over it) insist it is all pulled out and replaced by his people

  If indeed everything is good and the price is still cheaper than others, you'll be able to save the money or have other work done you didn't think you'd be able to afford
- The quote arrived on the due date. This gives you an idea of future efficiency
- If there was a delay in receiving it, did you get an explanation?
- Whether the builder visited the site to look things over for himself
- There was a covering letter. How does this read? What can you ascertain from it that could help you decide who to go with?

some people price only for labour and plant, expecting you to provide materials. This price will, obviously, not be comparable with others.

Contracts

If you're employing a main contractor it's essential to have a formal contract. The moment you agree with someone to supply you with a 'good' or service a contract exists. But this is just contract law in its most 'pure' form....the 'gentleman's handshake'. In my opinion, a proper written contract is vital.

Small works (less than £5,000) carried out by contractors or sub-contractors, probably don't need a formal contract, a Letter of Agreement will do.

When contracting with a builder for major works such as:

- Building a house
- Creating a major extension
- Doing a large loft conversion

Points to be made in your Letter of Agreement must include:

- A detailed description of the work to be done
- Clarification of who will be responsible for which parts, including who liaises with the council, professionals etc
- Confirmation of the building regs required
- What the project will cost
- Listing of the qualifications of the sub-contractors to be used
- How the work will be paid for, by whom and when
- How extras will be priced and paid for
- Start date and proposed completion date
- What you undertake to do before the tradesmen arrive
- How you intend to resolve disputes. Who will act as an independent mediator?
- Practical details about how the workmen will use toilets, make tea, park cars, use the garden, etc
- Any other matters that concern you

- Making a swimming pool
- Building anything unusual or technically difficult
- Doing a major refurbishment
- Constructing a basement
- Or anything that involves demolition

it's vital to have a formal contract. There are several good sources for standard contracts which could save you a lot of money. The Office of Fair Trading has a document that explains contracts and related issues. See www.oft.gov.uk and go to 'Guidance on unfair terms in home improvements contracts'.

1. The Federation of Master Builders (www.findabuilder.co.uk) will send you a contract by e-mail if you tell them the builder you intend to use
2. A local solicitor will have similar contracts that can be altered to suit your project
3. Some trade associations have standard contracts
4. Some local authorities have sample contracts

But the best is

5. The JCT (Joint Contract Tribunal) contract that comes in two forms – one if you're employing a professional to oversee the work and the other if you're not.

No contract is worth the paper it's written on unless it is detailed. The whole point of having one at all is to inject as great a degree of certainty and definition as possible into your dealings with your contractor so that if things go wrong you'll have some redress. This, in effect, means that the more detail you put into the contract the greater its value. All contracts must include final drawings; a copy of all required building regs; all safety certificates required (say for gas); copies of the contractor's up to date insurance certificates; a copy of any guarantees that come with the work; and a copy of your detailed specification (see page 51).

There are five main nasty areas that can cause trouble. It's worth knowing about these and being well prepared.

If you go the JCT route you'll get a pack containing:

- A sample letter to send out to contractors
- Two contracts, one for you and one for the contractor
- A set of guidance notes

Everything is well explained and uses the minimum of jargon. Each contract has two parts. Part 1 deals with:

- The work to be done
- Planning permission, building regs and party wall agreements
- Use of facilities on the premises
- Cost
- Payment methods
- Duration of the project
- Product guarantees
- Insurances
- Working hours and restrictions
- Security of the site
- Dispute resolution methods

Part 2 is about Conditions and includes:

- The contactor's responsibilities (including rubbish disposal)
- Your responsibilities
- What's to be done about Health and Safety
- How you agree on changes to the planned work
- How the agreed time span can be extended
- Who pays, when, how and how much
- What the contractor agrees to undertake by way of ongoing responsibility
- What happens if the builder (or you) goes bust
- How either party can get rid of the other and terminate the contract

Payment

You must agree who will be paying, at what stages of the work, how much, and the method of payment.

Disputes frequently arise over money. Not infrequently a contractor does his work perfectly well but the client refuses to pay, on some pretext. On other occasions the work actually hasn't been well enough done and the client quite reasonably refuses to pay. If you are not happy with a fraction of the work, don't retain half the money if 90% is due. Pay what is fair and take things from there (see below). All of this means being very clear from the start when payments are due, including how you'll pay if your contractor buys things for you. Agree whether certain payments can be made by credit card because most card companies offer insurance, which could give both you and your contractor confidence. These details must be in the contract.

Be very clear from the start when payments are due, including how you'll pay if your contractor buys things for you

Time penalties

Everyone worries about timing on a new build. You'll want to take possession of your new home and the contractor will want to get his money and go to the next job. It's in everyone's interests to get the job done on time. However, some people seek to tie their contractor down in their contract so he pays a sum of money if he fails to hit the completion date. Most builders dislike this type of penalty clause a lot because they can't know exactly when they'll finish, especially on domestic builds, where clients are notorious for changing their minds. It's often impossible to decide why a job has over-run and you may well have contributed to the delay more than you realise. How does your contractor charge you for this? No one talks about this other side of the equation. Supposing your designer throws a spanner in the works for some reason? Who's then responsible for the delays? And so on. It's a devil of an area. In general I try to avoid time penalties because they create bad feelings and can be impossible to resolve. If you absolutely insist on having a time penalty be aware that your contractor will price the job accordingly.

Renovation work and small projects are especially likely to run dramatically over budget as extras accumulate

Extras

Although the law of averages should mean that as some prices rise during the build, others will fall, this never happens! Renovation work and small projects are especially likely to run dramatically over budget as extras accumulate. Contrary to what you might imagine, really large projects are much less subject to such extras. This is mainly because they are so well planned and specified from the start. With lots of flexibility on time and money extras aren't a problem but the majority of self-builders aren't in this situation and dread the extras adding up. This usually means that as the job progresses they have to make decisions (usually painful ones) about what will have to go if the project is to come in on budget.

The trouble is that creating very detailed specifications ahead of starting your build comes at a cost, so insuring yourself against at least some of the 'extras hell' isn't cheap. The nightmare with extras is that they occur in a way that makes it hard for you to do anything but pay up. You can't realistically go off and get other contractors to complete the build, so your contractor has you where he wants you. All this becomes especially poignant if you've fallen out during the job, or have otherwise made his life difficult, because now is his time to get revenge.

In my opinion, whatever it costs, a detailed specification is money well spent, mainly because of the emotional pain it saves rather than simply the money per se.

A way round some of this unpleasantness is: to get written agreement on any extras before they are even started; to negotiate extras only with the main contractor (not their subbies); and to note all this in your Diary (see page 158).

So far I've looked only at unforeseen extras. But two other types of extras are commonly used in building. These are pc (prime cost) sums and Provisional Sums.

Pc sums are used when pricing a job where the specification is loose or non-existent. You'll see in some builder's quotes 'pc sum £600 for bathroom', for example. This amount is included in the quote but if you subsequently choose a £1,000 bathroom you'll have to pay the extra. The problem is that the £600 sum your builder had in mind was based on what he would expect to pay his supplier, and included him making a mark-up. If you now produce a bathroom from your supplier he'll lose out on that profit and will be displeased. All this should have been sorted out in your original contract well in advance.

Agree with your builder that you'll pay him the retention monies as soon as snagging is completed

Provisional sums are put into contracts and quotes where no one can be certain what the costs will be. The biggest hazard is unforeseeable bad ground. There may thus be a provisional sum for £5,000 'to remove excavated material', only to discover that the bill could be twice this because you hit old foundations and drains that have to be cleared. It's far better to agree contractually in advance how you'll handle such unforeseens (provisional sums) than to do battle later when things are fraught. If you want to waterproof yourself from all this expect the original quote to be substantially higher so your contractor doesn't lose out. After all, why should he?

Retentions

This is another very difficult area. It is common practice in small building work for the client to retain up to five per cent of the build price, once the job is complete, for an agreed period of time. But this must be negotiated before any work starts on site and be put in the contract. Some builders don't like retentions because it makes them feel distrusted. Others simply bite their tongue and add the agreed percentage to their quote. Many, though, are happy enough to accept the concept of a retention but fear they won't be able to properly define when the build is complete. Many self-builders are so keen to get into their house because their existing accommodation is costing them so much, that they push their contractor to let them in even before he's really finished. This makes his finishing more difficult and costly and the occupiers can also create new problems. Agree with your builder that you'll pay him the retention monies as soon as snagging (see page 194) is completed. Some will be happy to give you a sort of guarantee for six months and expect payment only then of this final sum.

Complaints

I've looked at this more elsewhere but here I want to mention it as part of the contract with your main contractor. The first step, if you're not happy about something, is to let your contractor know what it is and then to listen to him empathically (see page 16). He may well agree there and then to do what you want, or come up with some other perfectly reasonable solution. Bear in mind that you may not be entirely justified in your complaint. If this simple approach doesn't work, draw up a written list and make another appointment to meet with him formally somewhere. It can be helpful when going through your written list of points, to have someone else there as a witness. This individual could make notes of the meeting. If your contractor agrees right away to remedy matters, now he sees you're serious, this can be fine. After the meeting, send him your notes that summarise what you think was agreed. Say you won't agree to pay until matters are resolved. Take photos of any evidence.

If nothing happens within a week or so and your contactor belongs to an organisation that has a complaints procedure, then talk to them. Alternatively, you can suggest a third party acts as an arbitrator. Your local Citizen's Advice Bureau or Trading Standards Office will advise you how to find one. If all this fails, talk to your solicitor who can take proceedings or help you go to the small claims court if the sum is less than £5,000.

10 Extensions, Renovations and Conversions

The home extension, renovation, refurbishment and conversion market in the UK is the largest in the world, per head of population. There are also reckoned to be about one million empty homes in the UK, many of which are ripe for conversion or re-instatement. In addition, there are thousands of structures that are currently not used for housing but which could be, given the right planning approval ('change of use').

Extending your home

For every new-build in the UK there are probably four serious-sized extensions being done at any one time. This partly reflects the very small (by international standards) number of new builds. But there are also many good reasons for extending your home rather than moving or building new. It's usually far less disturbing for the family; is often a good way of enhancing the existing equity in your home; and can be just the right answer when the housing market is unstable or falling and your property hard to sell. You can be sure that the housing cycle will regain its stability one day and that you'll have a more valuable property as a result of your hard work.

Look at what neighbours have done, to see what you're likely to be allowed. If you want to do something that bucks this trend, be prepared to spend time, energy and money.

There's no doubt that building an extension causes disruption and stress because you'll in effect be living on a building site. But overall this can still involve substantially less aggravation than starting from scratch. It's also a fact that finding a site for a new home where you want it can be near-impossible unless you already live in an out-of-the-way area. Most of us want to stay near to schools, family and friends and extending can achieve this.

There are several basic options:

- Convert existing space (such as a garage) into living accommodation
- Convert your loft
- Build over an existing structure (for example, a granny flat over the garage)
- Extend your existing structure's footprint
- Go down into your basement, or create a new one

You can also build a completely new structure in your garden.

Before you decide to extend your home it's worth considering a few things.

Ceiling price

Whilst it's tempting to imagine that spending say, £25,000 will add that value to your home, this may not be the case. In most streets and neighbourhoods there's a ceiling price for any given type of house. It's possible to exceed this on occasions but it's far easier to overspend and then lose out if you're not going to stay for a long time.

I know it's very unglamorous and never the subject of TV programmes but it could be that the best way you can spend your £25,000 is by replacing your roof, re-wiring, painting and decorating, and making other necessary changes. This could, paradoxically, add more value to your home that an extension. Although most of us tend to think 'sexy update' when we talk about an extension, probably the best way of spending cash is, in this order: Ensuring the existing building is safe, structurally up to date and well-maintained; adding living space; and lastly, adding 'lifestyle'.

The best way you could spend your 25K might be replacing your roof, re-wiring, or decorating

In 2006, a Halifax survey found that the features people most wanted to add were not the items valuers ruled most advantageous to property value. People most favoured a new kitchen but valuers were emphatic that adding more floor area was more effective. To be fair, replacing a kitchen came second on their list. Other things they said added value were painting and decorating, extensions, extra rooms, and a new bathroom. Garages are no longer much wanted (for cars, anyway) and don't add much value but off-street parking certainly does. The value of some properties rises by 10% after adding parking.

People intending to make changes for their own use say they want to add: gadgets (such as flat-screen TVs); jacuzzis, hot tubs or saunas; a pool; or even a gym. But very few of these add value to your home when it comes to selling. Anything that creates extra maintenance can be an actual turn-off. The best example of this is a pool. Huge numbers of people are put off homes with a pool, the main reason being maintenance. As with all personalised home improvements, only ever do them if you are certain you'll live there long enough to enjoy them personally. How long this is, is hard to say but somewhere between five and ten years makes sense.

Room balance

I've looked at ceiling price and warned against over-extending. A word now about room balance. If you're contemplating an extension, be sure that the overall balance of accommodation is about right. Loads of bedrooms, with few reception rooms (or vice versa) confuses buyers. Also balance what you'd like to live in versus what buyers actually want.

Get an estate agent in before you go ahead with an extension of any size. They'll know what adds value in your area, or even in your exact type of house. Of course you can ignore their advice but at least you've been warned.

Closely allied to this balance is being careful not to ruin the architectural style of your property. Try to retain original features, refurbing them, or replacing them like for like when it's impossible to save them. Very clever designers can create additions that are strikingly different from the existing but the outcome can be hard to predict. The best of the old alongside the best of the new can work very well but both need to be cleverly detailed.

Balance what you'd like to live with versus what buyers actually want

When planning your extension or renovation be careful to get the flow of the living space right. Consider talking it all through with a good designer. Even if you don't intend to use one for your project, layout could be one area worth spending an hour on with a paid expert.

What else instead?

Rather than crashing on with the expense, stress and disruption of an extension, have you carefully considered what else you could do instead? Some possibilities include:

- Using storage or spare rooms for accommodation (dumping, giving away, or long-term storing the contents of the rooms)
- Thinking about the under-stairs area for a small home office
- Getting rid of your dining room and transforming it into useable space
- Converting the end of a garage
- Building something in the garden

Finally, a sensible alternative to extending might be to move home. Once you've looked at the realities (cost, time, energy, disruption, stress) of extending, think again whether it's really worth it. Are you trying valiantly to patch up your place to make it into what you want and need? Would you better off moving? If your life is stressed, difficult, or plagued by ill-health or other adverse circumstances, it's probably best to take advantage of someone else's hard work by moving on.

Rules and regulations

Just because you already own a property doesn't mean you can do what you like to it. You'll still need to think about planning, building regulations, and possibly listed building consent, if this applies. You'll also need to get formal permission from your landlord if your home is leasehold as opposed to freehold. It's wise to make this enquiry your first task as your landlord may quash the whole idea.

'I told you there wasn't room for that loft conversion'

Once you've decided what you want, it's a good idea to talk the thing through with your local planners. This said, you'll have seen that I favour professional advice as a short-cut whenever possible. An hour with a good local designer or builder could save all kinds of heartache with the planners because he'll be able to tell you at once what permission is needed, probably after a short visit to your home. You can then bat ideas back and forth without tainting your relationship with the planning department. They, after all, are not in business to give you free design advice, or indeed to ensure that you get the best bang for your buck. Only someone acting in your best interests can do this. Small extensions may not need to involve a designer at all as they can be professionally handled from start to finish by a competent contractor. Choosing one who's already done things for a neighbour is a great idea as you'll benefit from his lessons learned on their projects.

An hour with a good local designer or builder could save all kinds of heartache with the planners

Building regulations apply pretty much as to a completely new build but can be simplified a little as the new structure will become part of your existing home. For example, when it comes to energy-efficiency regulations you just have to build your new part to the latest regs. Newly-installed windows and boilers have to come up to the latest standards, of course. Part M (disabled access) is simpler because all you need do is to be sure your new work hasn't made it more difficult for a disabled person. Any house constructed after 1999 should already be Part M compliant.

Permitted development rights

'Permitted development rights' enable you to do certain things to your home without obtaining planning permission. In some areas of the country ('designated areas') these rights are very restricted and, if you live in a conservation area, the Norfolk or Suffolk Broads, a national park, or in an Area of Outstanding Natural Beauty you could find things very tricky. In some areas the local planners may issue an Article 4 Direction which means you can't do things that in other areas would be permitted development. If you live in a listed building you're into another loop entirely.

Basic considerations

What constitutes permitted development differs in each part of the UK and the Republic of Ireland. In England and Wales the following broad rules apply:

Volume:

You need to apply:

If your house is terraced
If it is in a conservation area
If it is listed
If it is in an Area of Outstanding Natural Beauty
If the volume is to be increased by more than 10% or 50 cubic metres (whichever is the greater) or
For any other kind of house outside these areas, the allowed increase is 15% or 70 cubic metres (whichever is the greater)

OR In any case if you want to increase the volume by more than 115 cubic metres.

Volume is usually the biggest hurdle to think about and is measured using the increase in external dimensions (not your increased floor area). You'll be surprised, on a small extension, just how much the wall thicknesses contribute. Advice on all this, and other permitted development issues can be found on www.planningportal.gov.uk

Height:

You need to apply if:

Your extension raises the roof above existing levels anywhere, or
If any part of the extension is more than four metres high (flat roof, three metres) and within two metres of your boundary.

There are separate rules for loft conversions. Loft dormers are allowed if the extension adds less than 50 cubic metres (40 for terraced houses) to the volume of the house. You can,

'Drains? Basement? I though we were doing a pool'

of course, apply for planning permission if you want your loft conversion to be bigger than this basic minimum.

General:

You cannot do anything that would bring your new front elevation nearer the public highway (unless there would be at least 20 metres between your new extension and the highway).

You'll need to apply if more than half your land area will be covered by existing buildings and your new extension together. This rule applies to the original house (defined as how it was first built or as it was on 1 July, 1948 if built before that date). This takes into account extensions that could have been done by others over the years. Most garden development can be carried out only on the basis that it doesn't become living accommodation. This means that to be within permitted development it has to be a home office, or something that couldn't be said to be a house.

Because so many day-to-day planning permissions involve relatively small developments/additions/conversions on private homes things were changed in late 2008 to bring down the barriers to include more in 'permitted development'. Always use a professional, who knows how to work the system, to get you the best result possible. Such a professional will also be helpful when negotiating your way through the Party Wall Act. This legislation governs what you can do to a wall (or other structure, including a driveway) you share with a neighbour. It applies to anyone living in a flat; or a semi-detached, or terraced house. Even if you come to an amicable agreement with your neighbour this doesn't mean you won't need to consider planning or building regs. Party wall regulations also apply to any new free-standing walls up to an existing building or astride a boundary line and any excavations you make that are close to a neighbour's property. This means the Act could affect you even if you live in a detached property.

Adjacent property owners can do one of three things: consent in writing; object in writing or; ignore you. If they do nothing within 14 days a dispute has legally arisen. The best way to settle matters is amicably between you. If you can't achieve this then you'll need to appoint 'An Agreed Surveyor' who'll draw up an 'Award'.

There's a lot of talk about rights to light. In England and Wales a right to light occurs if someone has enjoyed it from a particular opening in their building for more than twenty years. Get professional advice to help you make calculations about how much light would be 'stolen' by your development. These are civil matters between neighbours and have nothing to do with planning. A specialist company, Right of Light Consulting, can help on this (www.right-of-light.co.uk).

Design, Planning and Building Regulations

I've covered these elsewhere in the book but I'll mention a few wrinkles as we go along.

What's possible:

Going up: Loft conversions can provide meaningful extra space that's well suited to that extra bedroom; bathroom; store room; home office; or playroom. You'll need professional advice early on here as your roof structure and other issues may rule it out. If other, similar, homes in your street have one you're probably going to be OK. In general you'll need:

- Enough head height (ideally 500mm above your head or a minimum of 2.3 metres from the underside of the roof ridge to the ceiling in the room below)
- Enough width (about three metres or more between purlins – the horizontal beams that hold the roof up)
- A simple roof structure (one with 'hips', for example, encroaches badly on available space)
- Sufficient room to put in a proper staircase from the floor below
- No friendly bats in residence (they may be protected and thus have to stay put)!
- No chimneys obstructing your space
- Water tanks that can be easily re-sited (or you'll be paying many hundreds of pounds to replace your system with a pressurised one that needs no loft tanks)
- The correct party wall permissions if you intend to insert steels into your neighbours' walls

All these issues can be assessed by a good designer, builder or specialist loft conversion company in minutes.

> **In England and Wales a right to light occurs if someone has enjoyed it from a particular opening in their building for more than twenty years**

Escape in the event of fire is also strictly regulated but making such escape possible can mean making quite serious alterations to structures on the floors below. On occasions, the provision of a staircase and all the associated fire safety works can mean so many expensive alterations to the existing house that you may decide the loft conversion isn't worth the trouble. It's a trade-off. If your loft conversion is in effect a third floor (which it usually is) you'll also have to provide a window large enough to get out of in case of fire when a fireman's ladder is your only means of escape.

Current insulation regulations mean you'll have to install at least 120mm of a board such as Kingspan and this plus the ventilation requirements and ceiling lining will further reduce your head height. I overcome this on occasions by using an insulating, multi-foil 'blanket' (Actis make a good one) on the underside of the rafters. This is thin, yet effective.

If your roof structure is formed by trusses, there'll be more work and expense involved creating a suitable space in your roof than if you have a 'cut' (traditional) roof structure. It may even not be possible to do it at all.

Going into the ground is by far the most costly way of adding space to your home

Going down: Basements are very common in the US and in several Continental countries but rare in the UK. In fact, many highly competent professionals in the building world know nothing much about them. Building a basement as you construct a new property needn't cost the earth but doing so under an existing structure is difficult and expensive. Planners vary in their approach to basement conversions and extensions. Such works definitely require planning permission and can be the subject of heated discussions. In general, storage, hobby rooms, gyms and pools go down relatively well with planners, whilst habitable rooms do not.

Some older houses have basements that can be converted. These homes have suspended timber ground floors, which makes things easier than if there's a concrete ground floor slab. Going into the ground is by far the most costly way of adding space to your home as it involves: digging out and removing soil; ensuring the existing structure is sound and supported (perhaps by underpinning the outside walls of the original house); ensuring it is all dry (involving tanking and other more sophisticated water-proofing methods); supporting your existing ground floor and the loads of the walls on it; and so on. Providing light, ventilation, foul-water drainage, and access can also add challenges, though light issues are less of a problem today than they used to be if you use daylight coloured fibre-optic lighting, rob light from existing windows or use sun pipes. You'll need to create a space in your existing ground floor for a staircase down to your new space and this can often be hard to achieve. Going into the ground usually costs about double that of adding space any other way.

Going out: This is the way most people extend. A conservatory is a fashionable way of achieving this. It will bring light into your life but can rob it from the rooms off which it opens. There are issues too about heat loss. You are required to have a set of exterior quality doors between your conservatory and the room on to which it is built. If you want to do away with this you'll need to convince the building regs officers that you can and will make up for this loss of heat conservation by improving your glazing/insulation standards in other areas of the house to compensate. There's a general rule that the amount of glazing in a house shouldn't be more than 25% of the floor area but deals can be done by improving glazing quality and other heat conservation measures elsewhere.

For obvious reasons it's more cost effective to build two storeys whenever you can, as the high cost of foundations and roofing are then shared over the two floors. This said: you may not want something this big; it could annoy the neighbours more; it could make planning more difficult to get; and you may not be able to afford it. Most people's extensions are single-storey for these, and other, reasons.

Building challenges

Extending your home creates all kinds of problems that a new build does not. Even

There's a general rule that the amount of glazing in a house shouldn't be more than 25% of the floor area

quite seasoned builders say they'd rather do a new build for themselves than make substantial alterations to their existing home.

Access is always a problem compared with working on a new site. Parking and materials storage can be tricky, and problems with neighbours worse. Scaffolding may have to infringe on your neighbour's land or buildings, and it's often impossible to get meaningful–sized plant round the back, making hand digs more common. Your inability to store large amounts of anything will increase the actual cost of goods. In general, extensions cost about one fifth more than comparable new-builds on a site but this doesn't take into account the aggravation factor, which can be huge. Men around your home; dirt and dust everywhere, even with good screening; their use of your kitchen and toilets; worries about leaving your children in the presence of people you don't know; falling out with the neighbours; and security issues are a just a few of the headaches that go with creating a major extension. The whole thing is also under your nose day and night, perhaps for many months and if you're a 'private' person the sheer presence of so many people all the time can be unpleasant.

This said, some people like having their builders around and are sad when they go. For some extenders this form of building gives them what they want without a move and without the discomforts of living somewhere temporarily. It's also possible to keep a close eye on progress if you are project managing, and site security is less of a headache. Be sure to check with your insurance company before you lift a hammer. Your existing mortgage company will also need to know, even if you aren't borrowing cash from them to do the work.

Renovations and conversions

These can be an attractive option compared with building from scratch because there's something there already, which can make planning easier. You may also find that an existing structure has features that are worth

It can be sad to see the builders go

keeping, or indeed that make you want to do the project at all. The building's planning history can have a big effect on what you're allowed to do. Existing use usually governs its future use but this can be over-ruled by a special, government ruling ('material considerations') on a one-off basis. Previous refusals are usually a bad start but may not be terminal! See exactly what was refused and why. You may not, for example, want to turn an old dairy into the offices that had been refused. A better design, or your intelligent and persistent grappling with a problem could make planning possible for you when others have failed. If planning has been refused at appeal, or there have been several refusals over recent years, you'll probably be better off looking elsewhere. Not all existing use will necessarily work against you. For example, an unsightly, dangerous old building might be seen as best replaced by a good-quality family home, even if the general rule is that new homes in the countryside in the area are not encouraged. It is largely national planning policy (rather than local) that most affects those wanting to build homes in rural areas.

When converting or renovating in towns and cities you'll be expected to use materials that are the same as, or sympathetic with, existing ones

Once you've found your candidate property the first job is to have it surveyed. You'll need to know exactly what the state of the structure is and what you're likely to be in for, apart from the obvious things you can see for yourself. Unless the building is listed, you can make whatever changes you like inside. If it is listed you could be in for a heavy fine or even a jail sentence if you alter even interior details without listed building consent. When converting or renovating in towns and cities you'll be expected to use materials that are the same as, or sympathetic with, existing ones. And you won't be able to do anything that adversely affects the lives of those around you. Development in a village must retain the feeling of the area and not appear out of place in scale or design. Many local authorities are also pretty strict about the conversion of rural structures into housing. They'd rather see opportunities for employment created and so favour live-work units or even just commercial units. Some councils insist you make strenuous efforts to get business use before they'll even consider residential opportunities. Rural demolition and replacement is obviously the most controversial and can be very hard to achieve. Planners usually baulk at anything that means the loss of a building of local character; plans that increase the size and 'mass' of a building significantly; structures that are out of keeping architecturally; and so on.

This said, you may find demolition or making external changes very hard if the building is in a conservation area or other area of planning sensitivity. Really decrepit old buildings may just be too far gone to save at all. The problem is defining how bad 'bad' is. I have saved buildings that were near-ruins but this is very expensive indeed. Lots of test cases have been taken through the courts, as you'd imagine! It helps if you employ a local designer who knows the planners' track record on such things. There could also be deals to be done. We got planning recently for a client by offering 'planning gains' that benefited the local community in general. It was a pricey option but eventually everyone was a winner.

Development in a village must retain the feeling of the area and not appear out of place in scale or design

Most existing structures can be demolished to make new ground for a completely new build. The problem is deciding when it's worth using as much of the existing as you can and when it makes sense to take everything down and start again. Depending on your plans for the project it can be best to retain as much of the existing property as possible, especially if there are good architectural features that are specific to the locality. All this can be a very fine call indeed and even professionals may disagree.

The minute you decide to demolish, you're into all the decisions about plots (see page 30). But you also now have demolition costs to add to your budget, compared with having a green-field site. If you discover asbestos or some other noxious substance (which you might if the original building had been some sort of industrial or commercial premises), your costs can quickly escalate. OK, if you're lucky you might make a bit back by recycling salvaged materials from the old structure but this doesn't usually make a fortune. If you're recreating a building that looks like, or even has architectural references to, the previous structure it's worth keeping everything you possibly can during demolition and designing the old materials and features into your new build. Planners love this.

Planners don't want to see a cottage replaced by a mansion and talk about the 'impact' of the new house compared with what was there

The problem for many self-builders going the conversion and renovation routes is that they want something much bigger than already exists. In general, planners don't want to see a cottage replaced by a mansion and talk about the 'impact' of the new house compared with what was there. You may get something a little larger, or perhaps something that looks much the same further from the road or other public vantage points but is, in fact, larger. This sort of situation can often benefit from the wiles and skills of a professional planning consultant. All this is, to some extent, a game and there are ways of playing the game that give you a better chance of winning. Moving an existing property away from a road frontage; getting rid of other buildings on the site; undertaking never to apply for planning permission again for anything on the site; and so on can all increase your chances. As I write this we are involved in seeking a planning consent for a client in a highly sensitive rural and coastal location. The alternative could well be a small estate of houses, which we know the planners don't want. We are trying to get a large, one-off home for the site to reduce the local impact (traffic etc) for other local residents.

But whatever your plans for renovating or converting, be assured it'll cost a lot more than building from scratch unless you have a very high-quality existing building. Preserving the best of the old and building around it is costly and slow; re-creating historical features is painstaking and pricy; and everything takes a lot longer, from planning to construction. This said, I like converting and renovating because it's possible to end up with something characterful and special, compared with even a very good new-build. It depends how much you really want to go this extra mile, as to whether it'll appeal to you or not.

Whatever you're thinking of doing – extending, converting or renovating – talk to the neighbours early as they'll have views on the matter and could stop your development completely. (I talk more about neighbours on page 137.)

11 Project management skills you'll need

I promised in the Introduction I wouldn't be burdening you with any project management-speak. But given this is a book to help you become a better manager of your build, this chapter offers a few non-jargon guidelines. I'll focus my comments largely on those who've decided to build a complete home using direct labour, or perhaps to manage some other type of large domestic project. If you're going to employ a builder and let him take most of the strain, some of this chapter won't apply. A lot of it will, though – and probably a lot more of it than you think! After all, it's vital to remember that how ever many builders (main contractors and subbies) you employ, you are still the manager of the project as a whole.They may manage the actual build but you'll have to manage everything else....including them.

First, let me say that whatever the scale of your build and whether or not you've done anything similar before, you can only be true to yourself in your role as project manager. The more insight you have into yourself, the better you'll start out on your project. Because of this it's wise at the very first step – the conception of your project – to ask yourself some tough questions.

The good project manager

There are no definitions of the ideal project manager....many different personality types can succeed. But there are provable attributes and behaviours that are more likely to bring success.

Ownership

It isn't possible to be an effective project manager unless you take ownership of your project. This means much more than taking responsibility the way you would when driving your car: it has more to do with a deep longing and passion that not only keep you going but 'infect' others. This ownership will also keep you working hard and effectively, even when those around you want to give up. On one of my sites the men affectionately nick-named me the 'Duracell Bunny' because I was there working when they arrived and still there when they left. This nick-name wasn't just about my hard work but showed their appreciation for my sense of ownership of the build.

A desire for success and unhappiness with failure

In order to stay focused on the goal you'll need to care about success. As a project manager there is only one way to define success – getting the agreed job done, in the agreed time and on budget. As a human being you'll have other definitions to add to this. Notice I say 'unhappiness with' failure....not 'intolerance of' failure. Be assured your build will be littered with failures. It is inevitable, especially if you're a novice....and common even if you're not. Be kind to yourself when you fail, learn all you can from it and try not to

It's wise at the very first step – the conception of your project – to ask yourself some tough questions.

- How much do I really want to do this?
- How far outside my comfort zone will this take me?
- Could I achieve the same outcome in any other way?
- How passionate do I feel about it at the outset?
- Am I being bounced into it by someone or something?
- What reasons, other than the obvious one of building this particular thing, are behind it?
- What am I looking for from the project?
- Do I really believe I have the skills and the will to see it through?
- Am I expecting the project to provide 'life' answers for me that it cannot, in reality, deliver?
- What do those who love me and care about me have to say about it?
- What am I trying to prove to myself, or others?
- Have I the courage to back out, even though I've told others I'm going to do it?
- How will I know when I've had enough?
- What things in my life are sacrosanct... that I'm not prepared to sacrifice for the project?
- Are my personal relationships, physical health and mental state really up to dealing with this?
- What personal support will I have during the build?
- How do I normally cope with risk-taking? Could this be a risk too far?
- What financial back-stops do I have in place if things go pear-shaped?
- How would I feel about myself if I didn't go ahead?
- What else could I, or should I, be doing if I weren't doing this?
- I know I *can* do it....but *should* I do it?

blame others for your personal shortcomings. Bear in mind that the road to success is often paved with failures.

The building world, from one-man-bands to airport terminal constructors, is riddled with blaming. Main contractors and subbies alike seek to lay off the responsibility when things go wrong. Every trade wants to do their job in a way which best suits them. This often won't suit those who follow on....or you, the manager. Other people will definitely fail you...and you'll need to manage your way out of this with calm and elegance. It's vital to discover how and why things went wrong but blaming usually does no good. You have to rise above this and get a result. Encourage a management style that enables people who make mistakes to own up to them and still feel valued.

Being accountable – and responsible

As the boss of the build you'll take overall responsibility, no matter who actually does the work. If a tradesman repeatedly does things badly it's your job to get rid of him, of course. Or, as a good manager, to help him do it better. While the buck stops with you, you cannot possibly personally oversee the thousands of tasks being done in your name. When your architect or the building control inspector complains about something, it's your job to take it on the chin, discover how it happened and ensure it doesn't happen again. You are accountable not just to yourself but to your stakeholders (see below) and to those who work for you. This is what management is about. It's the job you have chosen.

Dealing with adversity

Most of us are good enough at managing when things are going well. How you cope when things go wrong, though – and perhaps desperately so – will show how good a manager you really are. I look at management styles on page 107. What's needed isn't perfection but tenacity in overcoming obstacles that would defeat others. And this can be difficult if you don't know as much as you should in an unfamiliar working environment. You'll never be any good at project management if you don't get a buzz

Handling stress well will get the best from your workforce

from overcoming obstacles. Never take this skill for granted. Give yourself a pat on the back, if no-one else will, and value your abilities.

Going the extra mile

In a way this harks back to the Duracell Bunny. If you have a good workforce they'll give you a fair day's work for a fair day's pay. You, however, have to go beyond this if you want to inspire your men and get the best out of their skills, goodwill and intelligence. When you go that extra mile, so too will they. There's a lot of what psychologists call 'transference' going on a building sites. People working on a site can form a very close community, with your key individuals working together almost like a family. They may well, albeit unconsciously, look to you to be the 'father' of this family. Some of your people will have father problems in real life and will, unconsciously, act these out in an 'as-if-you-were-my-real-father' scenario. Your dedication and willingness to put in that extra effort (as a good father would) can make their working life much more rewarding. Such people won't just like working for you today but will follow you to future sites too. If you can extend this good father role to taking an interest in their career development, and so on, you'll find they'll reward you with exceptional loyalty.

Managing from 'inside' the project

The days of top-down management are almost gone. This is just as well because as a novice you'll know only a fraction of what your men know. In fact they'll each know vastly more than you do about their own particular job.

This may not be the disadvantage it at first appears, though, because your job is to know your *project* better than they do. The principles of good management don't necessarily mean having a detailed working knowledge of each and every man's contribution. You're employing professional tradesmen and hopefully an architect or surveyor too. Trust your trades to know what they're doing, until proven otherwise. Call upon your professional advisers in the early stages until you are confident yourself what should be happening.

As you learn your job alongside the men, which you will, you'll slowly become more confident about managing them from inside the system. Go back to page 16 and re-learn your empathic listening skills. Your men will know you're struggling at times, and most will be gracious and decent about it. Praise them whenever possible and encourage everyone all the time. The men themselves will help you learn to manage them, given half a chance.

Good and bad management styles

Whatever your experiences of managing, or even if you've never actually managed anything, your own unique personality style will colour the type of project manager you become.

People working on a site can form a very close community, with your key individuals working together almost like a family

It's also true that we can all learn a lot from others. And some ways of behaving are provably effective, while others don't work. Here are a few guidelines on what works and what doesn't.

Good management styles

Listening

I can't stress enough how important this is. I dealt with this in detail on page 16. Here, let me say that the most important way of listening well is to constantly put yourselves in your employee's shoes. This is especially important when briefing them at the start of the job or an individual task. Listen to what they say. They'll be a lot more experienced than you and will want to know that you've heard their concerns before they embark on a task. Clarify, then clarify again, what it is you think they are saying. And listen with your 'third ear' to what they are really saying deep down. If a good subbie seems reluctant to do something, find out why. Don't let it go – only to discover hours later he's been struggling with something he wasn't happy about in the first place, or he's done it his own way and now you're not happy.

The most important way of listening effectively is to constantly put yourself in your employee's shoes

The next vital time to listen really well is when things change. Good tradesmen are used to things changing but they don't like endless change that prevents them doing their job in a professional way. Listen here to their wounded pride; their frustration; their impatience to get on so they can go to their next job; their fear that the task will go belly-up and they'll be blamed, and so on. Explain changes carefully and enlist the help of the individual tradesman or contractor to contribute to the way it is done. Change will certainly be a feature of your build, even if you were never to alter a single thing personally....and you will! Bear in mind that many people fear change. The reason you're doing a build like this is because you like change...or you wouldn't be doing it.

While listening, ask yourself all the time: Why is this person acting like this? How have I contributed to it? What does he need? How can I help? What can I learn?

Accepting that others have management skills too

OK, you're the overall boss but remember that your men, as individual small businessmen, will be all too used to managing themselves. Many of them will sometimes work on sites where management is scarce (or absent) and will be used to creating their own work plan and getting on with it. If you ride rough-shod over such individuals' tried-and-tested ways of getting the job done, you'll create waves and may even lose good people. Part of managing people well is accepting their 'difference'. We all tend to think that our way of doing or thinking is the best way. A few arrogant individuals even claim their way is the only way! But this is foolish, as there are many 'right' ways of doing almost everything. Keep your eyes and ears open all the time so as to learn how others do things, including how they manage their time and their work.

> **Part of managing people well is accepting their 'difference'**

Some of your employees, say a roofing subcontractor, will have their own manager or foreman. As when dealing with your main contractor's employees, always go through the foreman or the builder himself, rather than giving direct instructions to their men. By all means mention something to the individual tradesman directly but say you'll OK it with his boss first. The only time I routinely over-rule this approach is on matters of safety, when I say something at once whatever the political effect. A man-to-man discussion with your main contractor right at the start of the build will usually clarify how he wants communications handled. He may be managing several jobs at once and relying on you to hands-on manage things a lot of the time. He won't thank you for calling him every hour to ask about some detail that's worrying you. Some contractors, realising how difficult this is, have an arrangement in which their men call them if you ask them to do something they're not happy with. He can then come by and sort it out. If the subbie agrees with your suggestion, he'll just get on with it without making the call. Just bear in mind that when you tell your main contractor's men to do something, it'll be he who pays!

Showing leadership

There are thousands of books and whole university departments dedicated to this subject. Suffice it to say that on your site it'll help if you can not only be a good manager of the project but also, from time to time, show leadership skills.

Project management is largely about the micro-management of daily tasks and events. Leadership goes beyond this to encompass all your stakeholders, the workforce as a team, and the project as a whole (rather than the sum of its parts). Leadership is hard to define because there are so many ways that people experience being led.

On a building site, a good, effective leader:

- Displays a sense of overall ownership and passion that goes beyond the day-to-day tasks in hand. Leaders have a vision for their projects. This vision can have a positive effect on people in a way they find hard to define
- Creates a positive working environment that people actually enjoy, as opposed to seeing it as just a place of work. This ensures your men will want to come to work each day and will miss your job when it's finished
- Communicates with the workforce in an inclusive way that somehow makes everyone feel they have a stake in the overall project – not just the build
- Gives individuals their head to be creative and contributory, so they too can grow
- Generates a bond of genuine loyalty so the men will do their best for you. They are unlikely to do this for the project, but they'll do it for you if you've earned their respect as a leader

Handling stress well

I have to say that having a 'low-stress' personality will be helpful if you're taking on a building project. But there's a paradox here because a very laid-back individual probably wouldn't have what it takes to embark on such a venture in the first place....let alone succeed at it. Such people want an easy life and would sooner fly to the moon than run a building site!

In a sense, the very people who are most likely to take on such a massive project – especially with little or no experience – will be somewhat more susceptible to stress because they are in the business of setting a goal, then dedicating themselves to attaining it. They may also be somewhat arrogant, and suffer from more than a little hubris. These are both a bad start and can lead to stress.

Over my years as a therapist I found it useful to draw distinctions between anxiety, pressure and stress.

Anxiety is normal in unfamiliar situations or where there's a pressure to perform. All performing artistes say that without a bit of stage-fright they never give their best. Obviously when we're running a build we can't feel anxious the whole time but a few nerves can, at times, bring out the best in us.

Pressure is a phenomenon where there's a lot happening, but you're in control....and even get a real buzz from it. This appears to others to be stress but it won't be to you. You're on a high, making a lot of things happen at the same time and going home at night with a real feeling you've achieved something. Don't be seduced by others into thinking this is stress.

Stress itself is a more difficult matter. Unlike pressure, it makes you feel bad in some way (mentally, emotionally or even physically). This will need attending to as it will diminish your ability to function as a manager, or even as a human being. And if there's too much of it, you'll wish you'd never started. Saying this, I don't think I've met a self-builder who hasn't, at one stage or another, felt so stressed-out that they wished they'd never taken on the

Sometimes prayer is the only answer

project. If this happens to you, take heart from the fact that almost everyone does go on to complete their build successfully, even if they'd never do another!

Whatever your normal style, there'll be countless occasions when you'll be stressed during your build. All but the very calmest of individuals can be temporarily 'wrecked' by the goings-on on a building site. All modern life is stressful to some degree but there's something about the 'open air factory' element of building that makes everything seem more stressful than in other settings. In most normal workplaces there's a group of supportive people, including management, who deal with adversity in a tried-and-tested way that they have found works in a relatively controlled environment. On building sites, with an ad hoc workforce (who often don't know one another, let alone have loyalties to or affinities with one another) stressful events can assume gigantic proportions....and especially when you're a novice.

I have a saying that: 'If something can turn up in the wrong colour, on the wrong day, the wrong size and damaged...it will!' I have worked in several different industries and can say with certainty that I've never experienced the level of incompetence on such things anywhere else. The number of times an item will come to site chipped, broken or otherwise useless will astound you. It's still a mystery to me, even after all these years, how building industry suppliers function – let alone survive – given the frequency with which this happens.

When you've been waiting for weeks for an item, lined up specialist subbies and plant to install it, and got the right weather break for it all to be actually possible, your stress levels will certainly mount when the task is thwarted, unless you are some sort of yogic master! This is all made worse because the nature of building is that it is a sequential activity. B usually cannot happen before A, and so on. A setback such as the one I've outlined therefore doesn't just annoy you or set things back for that day....it can have ramifications that could even put the entire project at risk because of the knock-on effects.

When stress hits the job your people look to you to supply confidence. In an ideal world you should never show your own stress....but this is the counsel of perfection. It's instructive to remember that if a project were to go smoothly all the time there'd be no need for a project manager! The ability to recover quickly from stressful situations marks out the good project manager. But this is different when the project is your own baby that's tying up every penny of your life's savings. I find it a lot harder to remain stress-free when doing my own builds than when managing projects for others.

As the project progresses you'll that find timing, cash, scope, expectations and much more will change. Any or all of these changes can be stressful.

Ways of coping with stress include:

- Eating healthily and regularly...avoiding long periods without food or drink
- Drinking fewer caffeine-containing drinks such as tea, coffee and colas
- Ensuring you get enough sleep
- Making time for pleasurable things outside your build...keeping in contact with your hobbies, for example
- Taking time for a holiday...take 'builders' holidays' when they do
- Meditating or praying, if this helps you
- Feeling free to turn to others (outside the site) for support
- Learning to say 'No'
- Being gentle on yourself....after all, the world won't end if your project isn't going well
- Managing your expectations so they remain realistic
- Turning stress around, so you see it as an incentive to learn something
- Tolerating situations you cannot change
- Changing those you can
- Nurturing your friendships
- Trusting in the love of your partner, if you have one
- Avoiding jumping to conclusions or

making assumptions
- Improving your decision-making skills
- Focusing on the positive rather than the negative
- Giving yourself a 'reward' when you've done something well, rather than beating up on yourself when you haven't
- Delegating whenever possible...because you are not indispensable, or a Superman! The clever manager knows when to get others to do things – even if he could perfectly well do it himself
- Getting professional help sooner rather than later

All of the above help on a preventive basis, but what can you do, in the moment, when the stress is getting to you?

First aid for stress:

Take time out. Go for a walk off the site; take a long soft drink and sit in the car and listen to music, read the paper, or do whatever relaxes you. If you're doing very long days, just getting away from the site for a while helps put things into perspective. Shelve the task you were doing, and perhaps go off to a supplier for a change of scene.

Do some deep breathing. Sitting or lying down, and with your eyes shut, take a very deep breath in, with your hand on your tummy. Feel the hand rise. Exhale very slowly, feeling your hand fall. The secret here is to ensure that the very tops of your lungs are filled. We don't usually breathe this way and it feels odd at first. Keep with it. Repeat this breathing cycle ten times, and then relax for a few minutes.

Progressive muscular relaxation. Sit in the car and do some of the deep breathing I've just described. Now firmly clench your foot muscles for three or four seconds, holding your breath as you do so. Now relax your feet and breathe out slowly. Repeat this now with your calf muscles.... and so on right up your body: contracting and relaxing each muscle area in turn. At the end, sit quietly and breathe normally for a few minutes.

Managing conflict

When you're dealing with something that's costing a lot of money, taking large amounts of your time and energy, involving many parts of your personality and unconscious mind, and that you're going to live with for a long time, it's hardly surprising that your building work will cause a lot of conflict. Conflict is also very common when we're working at the edges of our knowledge and abilities and when we have to hand over responsibility to others. This is very hard for some people. Certain individuals find it difficult to trust almost anyone – and building work involves placing a lot of trust in the hands of people you hardly know.

Because our home has such significance to us, anyone who mixes with us at this time can trigger conflict. And this says nothing about the unconscious agendas of all the parties involved. Old battles within your relationship or your family-of-origin can now raise their head; problems you have within your own personality, your physical and emotional health, and personality differences with your builder, his staff, or your suppliers, can all add to the mix.

I don't mind how rich you are; how great a manager you are; or how much experience of the world you have – managing your own building project will be totally different from anything you'll ever have done. And here's one of the main reasons why.

When we buy a TV, or even a very expensive car, for the same value as a small building

Conflict is very common when we're working at the edges of our knowledge and abilities and when we have to hand over responsibility to others

project, we know what it will cost before we embark on the purchase. Building isn't like this. You pay for most of it before it's completed. The project is also built after you decide to buy, not before, as with almost every other product. Life is complex today and when we buy a TV, for example, the company will have done years of research, made huge numbers of prototypes and discarded those that don't work. And even then things sometimes go wrong with the TV you end up with!

Imagine now your build. It has never been done before. It has never been costed before. Even the very best builder will never have done exactly the same thing before. In fact, you are signing up for a prototype! But nobody tells you this. This lays the foundations for conflict. Imagine a factory where everything that came off the production line was a one-off. There'd be loads of conflict.

Preventing conflict

Preventing conflict is best of all.

Here are a few tips on how to do it:

- Encourage your partner, architect, neighbour, family member, tradesman, or builder, at every opportunity. This makes conflict less likely in the first place and increases the 'feel good' factor around the place
- Get the other person to air their grievances and concerns. Really listen (see page 16), and be open to other people's 'difference'. There are many to ways to be right. Few people, when they feel truly heard, continue to be aggressive or difficult
- Sort out conflicts with your partner in private, so your builder and other professionals don't find themselves engaging in amateur marital therapy. Present a unified front to them so they know where they stand and can't play you off against one another
- Have a laugh whenever possible, rather than being too heavy
- Be honest.....especially with yourself. Conflict arises very frequently when people have unrealistic expectations of situations. Sharing your fears or misunderstandings won't make you appear weak but will bring out the best in your professionals
- Be prepared to learn. The chances are you won't know more than your builder. Listen to him. This will make him feel a valued member of the team and therefore likely to want to avoid conflict with you
- Seek out trouble early and knock it on the head. This often means being brave and saying something before a minor problem escalates into a major one
- Take responsibility for your own emotions. Try not to dump your emotional 'stuff' on to your partner or your building team. Separate other anxieties and problems in life from the task in hand
- Try to compromise, if at all possible
- Be aware of the feelings of others. You may be the client but your builder and other professionals will have their problems too, be they at home, with their workers or suppliers, or with other jobs they're engaged in. Try to step outside your project, look down on the thing as if from a helicopter and keep things in perspective

Respecting people

As project manager you'll be doing a lot of paperwork but the main job is managing people. And you'll be doing this day after day for a year or more. The first lesson in earning the respect of others is to respect them. If you value your men, they'll respect you for your abilities and skills too.

A good tradesman will find a solution to a problem and be able to do something about it way faster than many an individual with a string of degrees. It is this, among other things, that I so value about my men. When there's a problem, I don't want, or need, anyone with a PhD in building science, I need a practical, thoughtful, problem-solver who can put his thoughts into action. And in my experience over the years, many builders are great at this. I am often humbled by this skill.

Supplying energy

Although it can be hard when the going gets tough, or you're not feeling on top of the world for whatever reason (perhaps nothing at all to do with the build), your team will look to you to be the energy source for the project. And understandably so. After all, if you aren't fired up by it, who will be?

Energy is infectious and makes not only you, but your whole project a nice place to be – even fun on occasions.

A part of this energy, while we're talking about fun, is humour. I use this a lot as part of my management style. If you get to know your men really well you can tease them and pull their legs in a way that lubricates the whole site and doesn't offend. You'll find your own style that suits. Quips I use often include: (on struggling with some new piece of kit): 'No worries...If all else fails, we can always read the instructions'. Or when a really able tradesman brings an apprentice in for the first time: 'Great to have a professional on the job, Pete.'

And so on. It also raises a laugh if you show your own vulnerability by putting yourself down in a humorous way. When I come in late for some reason (probably because I've been off somewhere else on something to do with the job), and they pull my leg about my time-keeping, I tell them how hard it is to get good people these days!

Sometimes, things get so awful that the only thing we can all do is laugh. Given that the

Whenever there are three experts....expect four opinions

The good manager never panics....
especially in dangerous situations

only alternative seems to be to cry, it's a good option!

Bad management styles

Obviously, a lack of any of the above. Plus:

The know-all

I realise some people act like this when they feel threatened or are at the limits of their abilities but it's an exceptionally unfortunate style on a building site.

First, unless you've been doing it for some years, there's no way you'll come anywhere close to knowing what your men know. Over time you'll pick up lots of useful knowledge and wrinkles and the men will accept them from you. But early on when you have everything to learn it's best to keep your head down, ask if in doubt, and don't come 'the big boss'.

Building is a highly complex business. The most dangerous man on the site is the one who doesn't know what he doesn't know! Many things defy common sense but are nevertheless right. Management methods that work elsewhere fail dismally on sites. When you're running a 'family' like the men on a building site, corporate-think has no place. If you've been, or even still are, a successful manager in some other setting, take your time to learn how a site differs from what you're used to. It's up to you to adapt to the industry, not try to re-define the wheel in an effort to make the industry fit your management model. You simply won't do it. I have run a publishing house, a film company, various medical situations, several businesses, and research teams. Yet none of these has been like running a building site.

The control freak

Again, usually a sign of insecurity, but still really annoying. Some project managers (and not just on building work) find the process attractive because they believe that having scoped everything brilliantly and drawn up a comprehensive work plan and a massive schedule, all will go as planned. These individuals, though, now see this as a shortcoming of everyone around them and try to enforce every tiny detail as if it were of Biblical importance.

> **Very often on a build, detail has to go hang for a while pending completion of something far less dramatic, fun, or even 'essential'**

Of course it is not. Try not to manage at such a detailed, obsessive level that you lose sight of the real job in hand. Very often on a build, detail has to go hang for a while pending completion of something far less dramatic, fun, or even 'essential'. By and large, most ordinary builders won't be all that interested in (let alone impressed by) your planning. They'll have their own plan in their minds for their work anyway. As one of my guys said to me once, on being given a huge pile of written instructions by a visiting architect, 'It gives me something to stand my coffee on, doesn't it?'

What I'm saying here is that project management isn't an end....it's a tool. And as with everything in life, there's a balance. Of course, there has to be enough 'management' to make everything happen but by over-managing, your site will become horrible to work on. Very large-scale commercial developments need this level of management, or they'd fail. But you're not running this size of enterprise. Frankly, no one would let you!

The bully

It isn't just building sites that have their share of bullies. They are everywhere. These so-called managers shout at people, terrorize them, humiliate them and instil fear into everyone, especially when the going gets tough. Almost nobody today responds well to this. And many simply won't tolerate it. Most good tradesman have more work than they can cope with and are very unlikely to put up with any mis-treatment from you.

Bullies are often power-hungry, which in itself goes down very badly. They want respect but go totally the wrong way about it. They think leadership is achieved by telling people what to do, and mistake people giving in to them for the respect they so crave. They also want their people to trust them but their bullyboy tactics have exactly the opposite effect.

The problem with anyone who rules by fear is that they sow dreadful seeds, the harvest of which they themselves will reap. For example, if your men are scared of owning up to mistakes, they'll start to cover things up....with possibly disastrous effects for the quality or even the safety of the build. Building isn't something that's ephemeral.....here today and gone tomorrow. The thing you're constructing will be there for a hundred years. Your mistakes will live on way beyond you to plague the lives of others. This is an awesome responsibility. Men who build in fear simply won't perform properly.

The day you discover you're the last person to know something's wrong, you'll know you're failing as a project manager. On a well-run site you should be the first to know, as your men do you the honour of sharing their mistakes with you and trust you to work things out between you. Anything else is an insult to them.

If you're trying to create a high-quality build, bullying will create exactly the opposite result. People working under a barrage of fear will deliver only enough to be sure to avoid being bullied. They'll never have the confidence to push themselves, to give that little extra quality or effort that turns a good-enough outcome into a brilliant one. This is a huge loss on a quality build.

If you find yourself bullying people, ask yourself why you do it, see how you could modify your behaviour and if necessary seek professional help to sort things out.

Men do you the honour of sharing their mistakes with you and trust you to work things out between you

The fire-fighter

We're all human and will, from time to time, have doubts about our abilities or decision-making. This doesn't, though, mean panicking when things go wrong. I've met managers over my whole working life who feel they're being effective only when 'fighting fires'. It gives them a buzz and they feel they're earning their money. They miss the point, though I can see how it makes them feel alive.

Good management isn't about fire-fighting, though on occasions you will need to do it. It's about preventing fires. A panicking manager is hell to work for and can be really dangerous on a building site. Even when something needs to happen quickly in a crisis, panic is the last thing you want with men working at heights, off ladders, with dangerous equipment, driving in restricted spaces, and so on. Panic here can spell disaster. It also gets the wrong window put into the wrong opening, and so on. There are no prizes for this sort of manager. He's a nuisance who should go home for the rest of the day!

As one witty tradesman on one of my projects put it – If there's going to be a panic, let's make in an orderly one!

The blamer

I've mentioned blaming already. It is a terrible management style yet very common in the building sector. In general, I work on the assumption that when things go wrong in any workplace it's the management that's at fault. You, as boss, should pre-plan and take account of risks in a way that makes it hard for your men to fail, damage themselves, wreck the build, or whatever.

We have to be very insightful and somewhat mature to separate our wants from our needs

Poor managers always look for others to put before the firing squad. But as an effective project manager you should be the first to take the blame, until proven otherwise. The alternative is totally unacceptable....blaming others when in reality, it's your fault. There are few things that poison a site more than this sort of behaviour.

Planning the project

In my experience, a substantial proportion of the stresses involved with having building work done come about because most people spend too little time and thought preparing. Probably more important still...most don't take enough time to listen to others.

I'll now look at the essential planning stages that all project managers have to go through, whether they're launching a new version of a computer game or building a house. I gave a taster of these on page 8 but here let's look at things in more depth.

Stage One....
Getting to grips with the objectives

What do we want?

Let's use building a new garage as a simple example. It might seem obvious that a garage is for storing cars. But few of us use our garages for this alone. Modern garages double as workrooms, hobby areas, storage/dumps, utility rooms, and play places for kids. Sit down with your family and see what it is you really want from your new garage. It might, paradoxically, have little to do with cars.

This is the best stage to have your family disagreements. Everyone will have a view, and many will be mutually exclusive. Even at this early stage, emotions come into play and need handling. Get everyone involved to write a list of what they want from the new project. Put these lists together and see how many needs can be accommodated. Only by doing this will you be able to brief an architect and deal intelligently with the planners. If, for example, your garage could possibly be large enough to have accommodation above it, either now or at a later date, this is a more ambitious project than a simple single-storey building and will need sorting out very early in your minds so you can approach your architect, money-bags and eventually the planners in a different way. This is the time to think ahead. Could the garage, if it's attached to the house, later become the ground floor of a two-storey extension for later family needs? If so, the foundations will have to take this into account from day one, even if you haven't got the cash to do the larger project now. Before you know it, Granny will be eyeing it up!

What do we actually need?

It's all very well agreeing what we'd like from our new building project but in the real world what we need is often quite another matter. The problem is that we have to be very insightful and somewhat mature to separate our wants from our needs. But unless you do this at the start of your project you'll be arguing with your partner and others in your family, not to mention the builder – who cannot possibly distinguish between your needs and wants, who hardly knows you early on. Stress levels will inevitably rise.

In truth, the way things are going in society with our inflated expectations about housing, we all have wants that are greater than our needs. If you are dreaming of a £40,000 extension, rest assured it will cost £60,000. At an early stage it'll be impossible to be realistic about costs because the chances are you've never done any building work before and you won't have a clue what things cost.

As you start thinking things through, be very wary about listening to the building experiences of relatives, friends and neighbours. They almost always exaggerate or even lie about the costs of work they've had done. Some will want to show off how rich they are and will thus give an inflated figure; others will want to show how clever they are at buying and budgeting and so 'under-reveal' the costs to prove what great value for money they got. But most likely of all, in my experience, are those who actually don't know what everything cost in the end. They live in a kind of denial on the issue. The oldest delusion in the book is to take the builder's invoice as the 'cost' of the project when relating things to others. In fact, very few people who've had building work done can accurately cost out their time, the huge ancillary expenses they've incurred, the opportunity costs, and the numerous non-building costs that go to make up the final price.

Also, when choosing a builder, your friends and relatives might not be as great a source of information and wisdom as they appear. Everyone has an agenda, and you'll need to be canny when assessing what you hear from those who apparently have your best interests at heart.

The concept of 'needs' in the context of your build will also vary a lot. Dad may need a project he can get his teeth into because he's bored to tears at work. Mum may need to show off her new kitchen to her friends and neighbours.....or prove, perhaps for the first

Never have more men on site than you need

time if she feels trapped in her stay-at-home lifestyle, that she can manage something large in her own right. Johnny may need to prove to his friends that his Dad is a big cheese. Jilly may need to feel heard about her ideas for how the place is going to look design-wise. Friends and relatives too will have their conscious and unconscious needs to be fulfilled. As a result, your project will become the focus of all kinds of people's needs for months or even years.

Who in the family should be consulted?

Back with the garage example: it could be that little Johnny is just getting into table tennis at school and sees himself practising at home so he can join a local league. Dad's hobby interest may call for a large workbench that would take up a lot of the available space, and Mum might be looking forward to getting a soft-top car that she doesn't want the neighbours' cats peeing over all night. It's easy to see that unless your intention is to build a vast structure, one or more of these family members is going to be disappointed. As boss of the project it's your job to start managing people's expectations as early as possible.

Should we tell the neighbours?

As soon as you think you've got the main bones of an idea thrashed out within the family, it makes sense to discuss things with the neighbours.

Most neighbours are flattered to be considered at this early stage – and it's in your best interests to do so. Not only do most of us hate to have something presented to us on a 'like it or lump it' basis but they could also have constructive ideas. I've been fortunate to have some excellent neighbours on various of my projects. In fact some were happy to recommend tradesmen, point out local difficulties, tell of their experiences with the planners, make it easy for me to park skips around the place, and so on. This can all be especially useful if you're new to an area.

When I'm involved in big projects that mean doing deals with the planners, the concept of 'planning gain' is common. In this we trade something the planners want for something we want. I think it's wise to consider the matter of 'neighbour gain' very early on. Is there anything you could do that would make life better for your immediate neighbours as you plan your new work? This is a great way of creating strong friendships with your neighbours and might make your life a lot easier. And easier always means cheaper.

What are the knock-on effects?

As with almost every endeavour involving more than one individual, there's always someone who stands to gain more than the others.

The 'disadvantaged' one now starts to count the cost, fantasises about what else they could have done with that sort of money, plagues themselves with other non-building-related power-battle areas and perceived injustices in the relationship, unconsciously tries to 'get even', and so on.

The time to talk all this through is well before you actually start doing any sort of building. If you embark on the provably stressful business of construction whilst fighting battles in your relationship, or in the family, you'll make any difficulties ten times worse for yourselves. It'll also cost you loads more money as builders and tradesmen pick up on the frictions between you and play you off against one another.

Following these guidelines should help even at this early stage. By the time you're in the thick of things you should be adept at these basic skills.

I think it's now helpful to write down your findings on all this. First, it's a great way of clarifying what you think you've learned; second it can be shown to your partner or other family members for clarification; and at

When the going gets tough it can be helpful to get this list out and remind yourself what your original objectives were

worst it can go into your personal records (see page 156) as a reminder of what you planned on day one. When the going gets tough it can be helpful to get this list out and remind yourself what your original objectives were. It can also be enlightening (and sometimes fun) to look back at once the project is complete!

Stage Two.....What are we trying to achieve and how will we know we've achieved it?

Although it might seem crazy to question what it is you're trying to achieve, it helps to be very clear about this from the start. Stage One of your 'scoping' exercise will have shown you what you hope to end up with: now you'll need to take this further by teasing things out into a whole project that involves more than simply a pile of bricks and mortar.

Let's suppose you're ostensibly trying to build a new house for your family. Try to be insightful now about this. What are you really trying to achieve? Is your relationship shaky and you're secretly hoping this will mend it? Are your children a problem and you want to make them happier? Is work going badly and you want to get fulfilment somewhere in your life? Are you trying to keep up with friends or relatives who've just moved to somewhere nice? How competitive are you? Are you hoping your build will make you money? And so on.

In short, what issues or problems are there in your lives that you are trying to solve by doing this build? Many projects the world over are expected to produce end-points that they can never, in reality, deliver. A new build can only deliver what it can.

Try to talk this through with your partner and the rest of the family if it seems appropriate. Ask yourselves how this new building project will alter your lives. How do you want it to alter your lives? What would happen if you didn't build it? How will your lives change for the better when you live in it?

If what you're planning can't stand scrutiny at this early stage, perhaps you're doing the wrong thing. All this will need tracking carefully as your build progresses, just be sure you're going the right way. Over the period of your build (say two years) your life and circumstances will change in many ways. Be prepared in your emotional planning to take this into account.

Having said all this, once you have all agreed what to do it's your job as project manager to focus on delivering the project as agreed. You can't be expected to redefine the wheel every few months. Managing the conflicts between people's perceived 'new needs' versus what's been agreed on and costed is part of your job as project manager but you'll have to police it carefully.

But one of the most tricky tasks at this stage is deciding how you'll know whether you've achieved your goal once the build is complete.

You need to decide between you what your steer is on the three main parameters of time, quality, and cost

OK, you've got the obvious result but was that, in truth, the only goal? How will everyone involved know if the project has been successful? As your build progresses you'll be making trade-offs and compromises the whole time. How will this affect your stakeholders' expectations...and by definition their satisfaction with the project?

Stage Three....Who will decide on matters of cost, quality and timing?

In the wider world of professional project management, many experts find it hard to know where their client stands on these matters. This produces real dilemmas from time to time.....and sometimes all the time! As the manager of your project it's vital for you to know what your stakeholders think about all this. There's little point you deciding, unilaterally, to go for, say, 'cheap' when you have to make changes to something, when your partner would rather have waited longer and got 'quality'. At this planning stage you need to decide between you what your steer is on the three main parameters of time, quality, and cost. Be prepared, though, to alter this overall agreement when necessary. There's no point being pig-headed for the sake of it. What you need is the ability to have an open dialogue asking the question,' Now that A has happened, would you rather go for B or C?' Depending on how flexible your stakeholder is, they'll either give you grief at you putting them in this position, or they'll constructively think around the alternatives with you. I know it can be very hard but as project manager you'll need answers if you are to empower others around you. There's no point your saying some event will put you back a month if you can't also give them an idea of what it would cost to get out of this dilemma. The sort of question that comes up all the time is, 'OK, this can't be as we agreed but what will it cost in time, cash or design to do something else?' Providing answers to questions such as this can take time and energy....and you're the one who has to do it!

Compromises then have to be made and both parties have to agree to let the matter rest there. It's no help one saying; 'If you hadn't gone for those expensive bricks we'd be able to afford the better bath'. The bricks are yesterday's decision and they're now part of the house. It simply isn't an option to take them down, clean them off and sell them to someone else so you can have the bath you really wanted.

This raises the issue of the amount of autonomy and control the key stakeholders are prepared to give you as project manager. You must be clear at this planning stage what exactly you are empowered to do without consulting others. It might be agreed, for example, that you can make decisions/ alterations involving expenditures of up to £500 without talking it through. Don't forget that one of the key stakeholders is your designer. He'll want to be involved in changes and alterations during the build, not only as a courtesy but also because they might affect his professional contribution and at worst create structural problems over which he will now not stand and that his professional indemnity will not cover. Your builder too is a key stakeholder and needs to feel heard at this early stage of planning.

Stage Four....Managing expectations

I looked at this briefly on page 8. Suffice it to say here that in the real world things change and what will be delivered at the end may not be what was agreed at the start, yet you and your stakeholders may still be completely satisfied. A key skill when managing people's expectations is not to surprise them. Keep everyone informed as change occurs and you'll be pleasantly surprised that even if you deliver less than everyone agreed they'll still be happy with the outcome. Of course you still have to deliver. This is your job as manager.

> **A key skill when managing people's expectations is not to surprise them**

All this means understanding how much risk you can manage. At what level do you involve other stakeholders in decision-making? How much risk are the other key people comfortable with? In reality you have to manage the project day-by-day so have to take responsibility for details all the time. Given that things will inevitably go wrong it'll be up to you to decide (perhaps after initial discussions with key stakeholders) what you report back to them and what you deal with on your own. People understandably get disappointed when things go pear-shaped but are much more tolerant if they've been forewarned. There are no excuses on a build like this for keeping things close to your chest and out of the reach of the key stakeholders.

If in doubt, come clean. Talk to everyone who could have an interest. In short, lay the matter off whenever you can, rather than keeping it close to yourself. People hate learning about delays and cost over-runs when it's too late to influence them. Take key people into your confidence sooner rather than later. Some self-builders find this hard. They see themselves as can-do people who shouldn't admit to failure. This is crazy, especially early in your self-build career. You'll need the help and understanding of everyone around you, not their anger or resentment. And anyway, it'll be about your fourth or fifth build before you have the confidence and knowledge to be able to make sensible decisions about what should be kept to yourself and what shouldn't.

An important tip when managing people's expectations is not to give them too many! Sorry if this seems cynical but it's a reality for all project managers in every field. It's far too easy to over-promise. One of the profession's leading project managers, who counts some of the world's largest companies and government departments as his clients has a valuable saying..."Whenever anyone presses me on something, I say, 'I'll get back to you on that'." Never find yourself bounced into making promises you cannot live up to. It might seem an easy way out at the time but it'll backfire on you in the end.

Building a 4-bed house involves more than 10,000 individual tasks

Far better to under-promise, then over-deliver. People love this.

Allied to this is being able to say 'No'. There are no prizes for persisting with something that shouldn't, or cannot, be done. If something's impossible, say so. You don't have to prove you're a Superman by striving to do the impossible. Be kind to yourself.

The harsh reality is that something may indeed be impossible for you but perfectly possible for someone else. This fact of life applies to anything at which we are a beginner. Be patient and one day the 'impossible' task may become possible for you. In the meantime you can only do what you can do.

Last, tell the truth. Building is a highly complex business and you'll be at it for many months or even years. Lies will come back to bite you. Keeping to the truth makes life easier and keeps you out of trouble with everyone ....especially the powers-that-be and the regulatory authorities. Of course you'll have to tell the odd white lie from time to time but to go further than this is to court disaster.

The main problem here is trust. You'll have many tradesmen, all kinds of suppliers, numerous professionals and so on, involved on your build. If you start lying about anything it'll become virtually impossible to know who you've told what and you'll get a reputation for being untrustworthy. You won't be able to manage effectively once this sets in.

Stage Five....What are the foreseeable risks?

Risk management is a key function of all project managers in every sphere of life. The purpose of assessing risk is to see what could go wrong in a way that would alter your ability to deliver the project on time and on budget.

There are literally thousands of things that could go wrong over your two-year project but many won't significantly hold you up or alter costs. Good risk assessment involves estimating not just what could go wrong but which of these so called 'critical' events will have a significant effect on your outcome.

The task at this stage of project planning is to put weightings on risks that could reasonably be expected to occur. For this you'll need the help of a professional. Your designer could be the best person, or you could enlist the help of a quantity surveyor specifically for this task. Judging what could go wrong and what is *likely* to go wrong on your particular project is, of course, a matter of some professional skill. And even professionals get it wrong.

Take, for example, bad ground. Your designer may have looked carefully at the site and even after digging trial holes still not be really certain that you'll get away with simple, cheap, foundations. But he'll be able to assess this risk better than you will. And this will help because once you've done your risk assessment you'll be able to allot a sum of money (or percentage of the project cost) that you can keep as a kitty from which to draw when things go bad. I look at contingency sums on page 73.

On a straightforward small build it can be sensible simply to put aside say ten percent of the build budget for unforeseens. If you are using untested building methods, or there are special circumstances to your build, this sum will need to be a lot larger. One build I ran involved creating huge sea walls and jetties. The whole task meant working around the rise and fall of the tides, and these changed within any given month. Assessing the risk factors here was very hard, and it was near-impossible to predict the impact of a machine getting bogged down and flooded with sea water for three days!

Risks you'll be likely to encounter include: running out of money; hitting unforeseeable problems, such as with foundation work; bad weather; disputes with your workforce; unreliability of your workforce; suppliers that don't supply what or when they say they will; fights or disputes with professional advisers; legal battles; planning delays; dealing with new or relatively untried building methods; problems with complex systems; you, a key worker or a professional adviser having an accident or serious illness; problems with neighbours; and much more. I look at how to handle many of these on pages 182-193.

Some of these risks you can lay off on others, for example by taking out adequate insurance cover. Once you've discussed the realities of your specific risk with a suitable professional, see what your insurance broker can offer. Good professionals have sources of insurance for all kinds of risk. It's up to you to decide what you want to do about it!

But simply assessing what risks there might be isn't enough. You now need to look at how you would manage your way out of each problem should things go wrong.

Say you have decided on a particular window company in Holland. It makes sense now to decide what you'll do if these windows are delivered one or two months' late, or not at all! What if they all come in the wrong sizes? What will you then do? Talk with your designer about such key issues and start to look at what critical events could hold you up, or even close your site completely. Work out contingency plans for what will actually happen in such an event. This can, though, be the counsel of perfection. I've just had a nightmare with a window company when even our best-laid contingency plans failed. Events can sometimes conspire to make it impossible to implement your contingencies. This doesn't mean it isn't best, on balance, to make them.

Suppose you get ill and can't work for a month? What are your plans to cope with this?

And so on.

Drawing up your risk management document will give everyone a lot of confidence and should reduce your stress levels a lot.

12 Creating a team

No matter if you intend to lay every single brick of your building yourself – and very few self-builders do – an early task is to start creating your team. Building a house involves many professionals and tradesmen, all of whom will look to you for leadership, vision – and an income!

The secret, as with any task, is to get the right people with the right skills to do the right jobs. I look on page 104 at the day-to-day management of this team.

Most of us managing small domestic builds find it's best to have as few people actually working on the site at any one time as possible (compatible, of course, with getting the job done in a reasonable time). When planning your team, don't get carried away with the notion that having twice as many bodies around will get the task done twice as fast. This is rarely the case unless the site is really large or, for example, consists of many floors where individual trades can work unaffected by others. On balance, the more men, the less the amount of productive work gets done. More people usually means: more personnel problems; more 'cross-infection' with bad habits such as poor time-keeping, laziness, idle chatting, prolonged tea-breaks, etc; getting in one another's way physically; opportunities for accidents; and so on.

The team members you'll need will include:

- An accountant
- A solicitor
- A 'tame' estate agent
- A surveyor
- A designer
- Possibly a planning consultant
- Possibly a quantity surveyor
- Your building control inspector
- A source of cash (unless you are using your own resources)
- A friendly bank manager
- A helpful partner (if you have one)
- A good builder, or the equivalent directly-employed trades
  - Plumber
  - Electrician (sparks)
  - Carpenter (chippie)
  - Ground workers
  - Plasterer (spread)
  - Brick/block layer (brickie)
  - Labourer
- Specialist subcontractors (subbies)

On most straightforward domestic sites, once you get more than about six people working together things start to deteriorate and are more difficult to manage. At the very simplest level, events can happen so fast that, as a beginner, you won't be able to keep track of, or influence, them. Slow, steady progress is an advantage for the rookie builder because both your mistakes and those of your men can be detected soon enough to be able to do something about them cheaply.

I look at good management styles on page 104 but whatever your style, there are certain things that every member of your team will need to be aware of:

- What their role is and exactly what's expected of them
- Who they report to
- Who they look to for instructions on a day by day basis
- Who they'll need to interact with on the team in order to do their work
- How they are to be employed
- Who will pay them and how
- Who they complain to when things go wrong or they aren't happy
- How they'll know when they've done the job the way you want it
- How they can contribute creatively to the build process
- Your site rules and discipline (see page 149)
- Your overall vision for the project

Bear in mind that this team you're bringing together will never have worked before on your project. They will, of course, have worked on other people's. This means they'll bring all kinds of invaluable experience to the party – experience from which you can learn. The secret for you as a rookie builder is to learn all you can while avoiding other people's agendas. This is a very steep learning curve!

The basic unwritten rule of building is that all parties want things to be done their way because it is familiar and easier for them. Your job is to see that the overall task gets done while smoothing out friction between trades who, by and large, want to do a fair day's work and get off to their next job. In a way, whether you are employing a main contractor or directly employing subbies, your task is to create an environment that makes your build seem special and worth their while coming into work every day. Most good subbies can choose to work anywhere, so great is the demand for high-quality tradesmen. Your job is to make them feel that your build is that bit different and thus more attractive.

The main way you can achieve this is in the way you manage your team. And unlike many teams in the normal workplace, this one of yours will be very fragile, temporary and lacking in loyalty to one another. In a sense you'll need to create your own 'brand' for your build. People who would otherwise find it hard to feel any sense of loyalty to a job of work will find it easier and even desirable to be loyal to this brand. This management task is a hard one but if you stick to my list above, and use all your leadership skills, you'll soon find that people create a kind of site/brand loyalty that means something to them. It is in your interests to promote this in any way you can, through good times and bad.

Your team will bring all kinds of invaluable experience to the party — experience from which you can learn

At the heart of this management style will be the way you motivate your men. In some ways your task will be harder than anything you've done before because you may find you'll have little intrinsic authority on your build. If you're normally an accountant or a shop-keeper you'll be used to people understanding and, hopefully, respecting your knowledge and skills base. This gives you at least some basic authority in that situation. What many rooky builders find is that they have no intrinsic authority on their site as every one else knows more than they do and some people actually resent being instructed by someone they don't respect. But you can build this respect and even authority as you demonstrate that you are a good project manager, even though you know only a fraction of what any of your individual tradesmen know.

Creating this authority comes with time and practice and involves learning certain management skills (see page 104). I find that authority usually follows respect. This means first earning the respect of your team. Getting the best out of people in this sort of situation involves both stick and carrot. I've had subbies tell me that for enough cash they'll put up with a heck of a lot of aggravation and inept management from bloody-minded bosses. Others say that no amount of money can compensate for poor management – they'd sooner work on a site where someone knows what's going on! Some people need more stick than others. And a few tolerate no stick at all! I work on the principle that most people: are decent; want to do a good day's work; enjoy what they're doing; can be motivated, given a little effort; thrive on encouragement; and don't like to fail.

All of this applies equally to your contractor, if you are employing one. Look at page 77 where I look in some detail at what makes builders tick. This will help you get the best out of your contractor.

However you achieve it, ensure that each member of your team feels valued and trusted and takes on *your* goal as their personal one, too. We all have varying and different levels of motivation and some people will need no motivation from you. Such a tradesman will largely organise and monitor his own work, will know his limitations, be delighted to add value by suggesting creative ideas or ways of saving you money, and so on. Others will need more effort from you to get them going and keep them going.

Setting mini goals can greatly help in keeping motivation high. The building of a four-bed detached house involves more than 10,000 individual tasks. Try to create end-points that everyone can aim for. Praise the team when they get there, especially on time, and use that jumping-off point as the start of the next chapter in the build. This breaks down the

When a couple work well together, the builders don't stand a chance

huge tasks into bite-size pieces that most people can relate to. Try to make even the lowliest player feel valued in their contribution to the achieving of this mini goal. People tend to forget, for example, that site labourers are gold dust. OK, they may not have the skills-base of seasoned tradesmen but their contribution can make or break a site. Their worth needs to be recognised and valued.

One of the best single sources of motivating is good communication. I look at this below.

I always try to motivate by ensuring that individual workers feel they're getting something special out of my builds. Try to give an individual a task that'll stretch him just that little further so he ends that day having learned something new. Everyone likes to take lessons learned on to their next site as it makes them more attractive to their next employer. We can easily spend a lifetime in building learning new tricks, about new materials, new methods and so on. Stretching your contractor or tradesmen will enliven them and make what could have been a boring repetition of something they've done a thousand times seem special.

In all of this, keep your eye on team relationships. Keep a watch out for friction and see what you can do to alleviate it. Everyone will have some sort of gripe at some stage during your build. Listen carefully to what they have to say (see page 16) and do what you can to pour oil on the troubled waters. This might mean re-scheduling tasks so people who don't get on easily can do things at different times.

Be seen to be even-handed, rather than having favourites. Find something warm to say to those who are finding it hard relating to others. Difficult behaviour can usually be understood if you give the individual a little time. Maybe suggest going out for a pint after work. Just sitting down, one-on-one with a cup of tea can often work wonders. I look more at discipline on page 149.

13 Communication

Building is largely a people business. It involves individuals of very different personality styles, ages, intelligence levels, professional skills, expectations, experience, self-discipline and earning power. It's impossible to say whether your plumber is 'worth' more than your accountant; or your designer more than your brickie. Each plays his essential part in the team and, as with all teamwork, your build's final result should be more than the sum of its parts. It is up to you as conductor of this orchestra to ensure that this is the case.

Dealing with such disparate individuals, from a highly articulate and intelligent solicitor to a semi-literate labourer, can call for all your management skills. Many's the time I've had to alter the way I communicate once I realised an individual couldn't read or write with any confidence. I've said elsewhere that I think formal education and intelligence is over-rated on a building site. I'm frankly not that interested in how formally educated my tradesmen are. I value other things they have to offer.

There's a huge amount of wisdom and knowledge in your manual workforce without which your project will surely fail. Such individuals may need to be communicated with in a way that's unfamiliar to you, if you've come from a middle-class or professional background where people thrive on written communications, meetings, notes and so on. Finding the right 'voice' can be hard for some self-builders. They feel strange being one of the lads yet don't want to 'come the heavy boss' either. Just take things slowly. Be sensitive to the feedback you get from your men and you'll find a happy place where you'll fit in to the mix. You are, after all, dropping in to their world.

Communication is at the very heart of a happy, productive, safe, building site.

Meetings on a small domestic site are usually informal and involve few people. It'll be rare for you to call all your men together but informal get-togethers can achieve a lot. Most 'meetings' will be between yourself and an individual or two. It makes sense to record what was agreed (unless it's something very trivial) in your Diary. More formal meetings with outside professionals (including your own designer) should be noted and action points listed in your Diary. If you need a subbie to be present at a formal meeting, be sure to give him enough notice if he's not working on your site full time.

Most people employing a main contractor like to meet him almost every day. This keeps tabs on the nitty-gritty detail as it arises. Depending on the nature and stage of the project, this daily chat might be too frequent. More frequent and intense get-togethers will be necessary as the second fix develops and detailed fitting-out decisions need to be made. It makes sense to have a proper weekly meeting to take stock of progress and setbacks and for him to let you know what's expected of *you* in the coming week.

Basic rules of effective communication include:

- Listening to everyone at their own unique level, and doing so empathically (see page 16)
- Being aware of the team dynamics so you can intervene effectively when necessary
- Letting those who need to know, exactly what you are doing and why
- Being clear about what you want an individual to do and why
- Feeding back information from the outside world to those individuals who need to know. News from your dealings with the planners, building regs inspectors, the press, or whomever, all add to the fun of the build. People like to have common enemies and whinging about the planners or other officials can do a lot for team morale!
- Taking people into your confidence about the project as a whole
- Seeking people's advice and comments
- Asking how they would do things differently, if it were their build
- Keeping everyone informed of delays, money problems, and trouble in general. You'll be surprised how decent and understanding most people are if you come clean with them. I've had cause to be grateful on occasions when, on being told of a cash-flow problem, my men have volunteered to wait for their money
- Remembering that what goes round, comes round. People who feel heard and valued will try that bit harder
- Supporting your people when they have personal or health problems. OK, you're not running a therapy centre but it doesn't cost anything to do the decent thing, perhaps allowing someone time off to go to the hospital to see a sick relative when you'd really rather have them at work, or listening to their worries about their girlfriend's car crash
- Keeping everyone in the picture on the project as a whole. It's easy for subbies to get bogged down in their own small part of the build. They are usually delighted and interested to feel involved in the project as a whole
- Keeping everyone informed as change occurs. Seek advice from those whose opinions you value. Also keep your ears open for the opinions of those you wouldn't have thought as making a contribution. You could be surprised
- Communicating with your family, partner and other off-site parties. Get anyone who has an interest down to the site from time to time to maintain their commitment. Don't forget that your nose is in the trough every day but it can be a lot harder for friends and family to believe in the project in the way you do. They may just see you as tired, bad-tempered, worried, or whatever and would love to have the opportunity to see for themselves what it's all about. Once they get a grip on what you actually do all day they'll be more appreciative and understanding
- Be sure to keep up your communications off the site. Try to spend time with friends, so you don't become a one-string fiddle obsessed with his build. Re-charge your batteries by getting people to listen to you. You'll be giving a lot as project manager and someone somehow will need to help you get your energies back. An intimate friend or life partner can help

14 Planning the work

Having looked at the key management skills you'll need, it's now time to see how you'll manage your actual build. Please note that the formidable list below is all *your* management work....and not a single brick has yet been laid! Whoever said that if you have your house built by a contractor there's not much for you to do?

Self-building is a daunting process for most people because they need to borrow money and their lending institution will release only certain amounts of it at various, pre-agreed, stages of the build. This means that you as the builder (or your main contractor) will need to know when you'll need the cash. As can be seen from the table below, an average-sized family house build can be divided into ten roughly equal stages spread over about ten months. For most normal builds using standard materials these stages cost about the same. They take different times, however.

Your time-line

Create a simple time-line chart for yourself using the computer-based model on page 130 as a template. Once you've done it, pass it by your designer to check he agrees. He'll tell you where you're likely to need more time, and modify this simple chart accordingly. He, or a project manager, may supply you with a computer-generated document that shows almost every stage of your build in much more detail. Some good builders offer this service too. Unless you especially enjoy it you could get this time line done by a pro from the start. The clock of your time line starts ticking once you are ready to get on the site and have the funds to hire people.

Stages I've already covered that will get you ready for planning your work include:

- Considering scope, time, cost and quality (page 8)
- Deciding what you want and what you need (page 116)
- Deciding what you're going to do (page 116)
- Getting the money together (page 22)
- Costing everything (page 25)
- Finding a plot (page 30)
- Getting your budget together (page 35)
- Choosing your designer (page 42)
- Designing your home (page 39)
- Specifying everything (page 51)
- Sorting out Building Regs and Planning (page 55)
- Starting off your record keeping (page 156)
- Getting insurances and warranties (page 74)
- Choosing a builder (page 84)

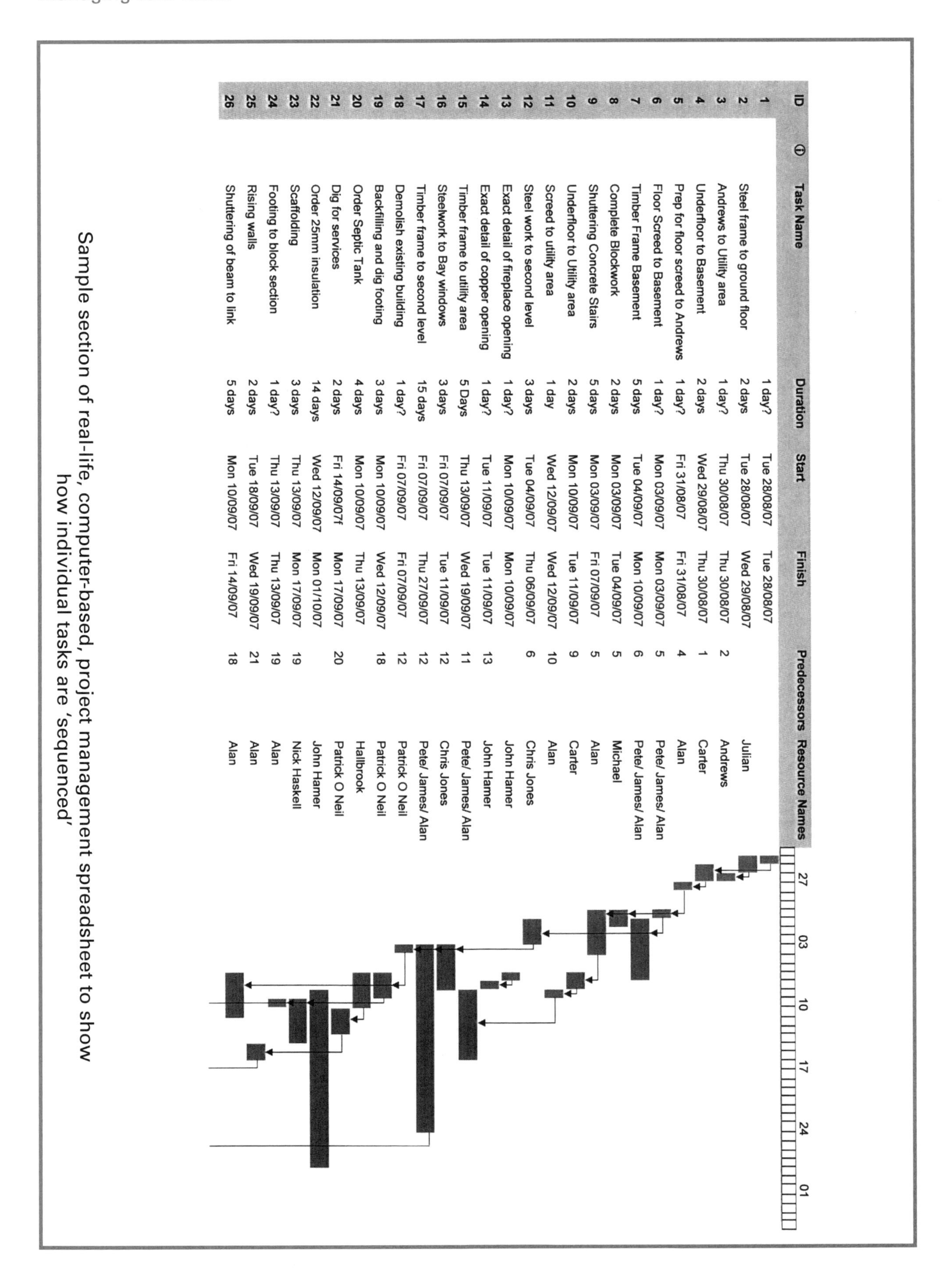

ID	ⓘ	Task Name	Duration	Start	Finish	Predecessors	Resource Names
1			1 day?	Tue 28/08/07	Tue 28/08/07		
2		Steel frame to ground floor	2 days	Tue 28/08/07	Wed 29/08/07		Julian
3		Andrews to Utility area	1 day?	Thu 30/08/07	Thu 30/08/07	2	Andrews
4		Underfloor to Basement	2 days	Wed 29/08/07	Thu 30/08/07	1	Carter
5		Prep for floor screed to Andrews	1 day?	Fri 31/08/07	Fri 31/08/07	4	Alan
6		Floor Screed to Basement	1 day?	Mon 03/09/07	Mon 03/09/07	5	Pete/ James/ Alan
7		Timber Frame Basement	5 days	Tue 04/09/07	Mon 10/09/07	6	Pete/ James/ Alan
8		Complete Blockwork	2 days	Mon 03/09/07	Tue 04/09/07	5	Michael
9		Shuttering Concrete Stairs	5 days	Mon 03/09/07	Fri 07/09/07	5	Alan
10		Underfloor to Utility area	2 days	Mon 10/09/07	Tue 11/09/07	9	Carter
11		Screed to utility area	1 day	Wed 12/09/07	Wed 12/09/07	10	Alan
12		Steel work to second level	3 days	Tue 04/09/07	Thu 06/09/07	6	Chris Jones
13		Exact detail of fireplace opening	1 day?	Mon 10/09/07	Mon 10/09/07		John Hamer
14		Exact detail of copper opening	1 day?	Tue 11/09/07	Tue 11/09/07	13	John Hamer
15		Timber frame to utility area	5 Days	Thu 13/09/07	Wed 19/09/07	11	Pete/ James/ Alan
16		Steelwork to Bay windows	3 days	Fri 07/09/07	Tue 11/09/07	12	Chris Jones
17		Timber frame to second level	15 days	Fri 07/09/07	Thu 27/09/07	12	Pete/ James/ Alan
18		Demolish existing building	1 day?	Fri 07/09/07	Fri 07/09/07	12	Patrick O Neil
19		Backfilling and dig footing	3 days	Mon 10/09/07	Wed 12/09/07	18	Patrick O Neil
20		Order Septic Tank	4 days	Mon 10/09/07	Thu 13/09/07		Hallbrook
21		Dig for services	2 days	Fri 14/09/07f	Mon 17/09/07	20	Patrick O Neil
22		Order 25mm insulation	14 days	Wed 12/09/07	Mon 01/10/07		John Hamer
23		Scaffolding	3 days	Thu 13/09/07	Mon 17/09/07	19	Nick Haskell
24		Footing to block section	1 day?	Thu 13/09/07	Thu 13/09/07	19	Alan
25		Rising walls	2 days	Tue 18/09/07	Wed 19/09/07	21	Alan
26		Shuttering of beam to link	5 days	Mon 10/09/07	Fri 14/09/07	18	Alan

Sample section of real-life, computer-based, project management spreadsheet to show how individual tasks are 'sequenced'

There are eleven well-recognised stages to a domestic build. They apply whether you are building an entire house or extending your kitchen, for example.

- Groundworks: including site preparation, access road, foundations, drainage and main underground service supplies, ground floor slab
- Ground floor walls (external and internal masonry ones), first-floor structure
- Scaffolding, first-floor walls and forming the roof structure, chimneys
- Covering the roof
- Installing windows and external doors (makes the place water-tight)
- Internal stud walls, rainwater goods, fascias, soffits
- First fix plumbing and electrics
- Plastering, screeding, and second fix carpentry
- Second fix electrics, fitting kitchen and cupboards
- Second fix plumbing and finishing, decorating, tiling
- Snagging, finishing, external works

If you're building a complete house, all this work (about twenty main jobs) can be accomplished by a dedicated team of three or four men working full-time for thirty or so weeks. This is what a professional building company would allow. If you are using direct labour, though, they all have their own professional lives to lead so you'll find it hard to dovetail everyone into a schedule that suits your desired timetable. And you won't be used to overlapping tasks in the most efficient way. In reality, there could be twenty or more people working on your job over a period of a year to eighteen months. And this is if all goes well. If you're using specialist subbies for particular jobs; unorthodox building methods or materials; want a very eco house or a very high-tech one; or have unforeseen setbacks; the number of people and the time it all takes will certainly increase.

Sequencing

The many scores of tasks within each of these twenty main jobs cannot, of course, be carried out end-to-end or you'll be on your site for years. The secret is knowing how to overlap jobs. The really effective project manager plays this game of three-dimensional chess like a master so as to get the job done on time and on budget. The spreadsheet on page 130 gives a feel of this sequencing.

Sequencing entails knowing, in detail:

- The title of each task, and assigning it a job number
- What the task entails
- How long it will take (best and worst scenarios)
- Who will do it
- Their lead time for availability
- What critical work needs to be completed before they can start their job
- What back-up or associated trades they require to do their task
- What you will do yourself

Building the average four-bed family house involves somewhere in the region of 10,000 individual tasks. Of course most of these go smoothly. The skill when project-managing a new build of any kind is being aware of the relatively few critical areas that will cause serious headaches if they go wrong. Talk to your designer about this. Knowing your proposed build he'll be able to advise you from his experience exactly where you can expect such hold-ups.

All the topics mentioned on pages 182 to 193 can pose serious potential risks to your critical path. Knowing this, you'll be able to take avoiding action or have stand-by plans so your build is held up as little as possible.

EXAMPLE OF SEQUENCING AN ACTUAL TASK...THE INSTALLATION OF SIMPLE GROUND AND FIRST FLOOR STEELWORK

Title of task
Steel frame to ground and second floors to take window units (job no 28)

What it entails
XX Steel Co supplying steel; YY Steel Erectors Co to erect

How long it takes
Best, 1 day; worst, 2 days

Who will do it
XX Steel Co to deliver material to site on (date)
YY Steel Erectors to come following Monday (date)

Lead times
Structural engineer needs 2 weeks to do design (on holiday from 00 to 00)
XX need 8 weeks to do their design work, fabricate and galvanise steel. Warning! They are having trouble with their galvanisers and this could slip by two weeks
YY need 4 weeks' notice of erection date

Critical preparatory work

- Jim must have concrete foundation pads in place with bolts set in one week before erection (dimensions/positioning/height of pads, and bolt positions checked by Jim and me at least two days before steel comes)
- Book ZZ Crane Co to be on site at 08.00 to off-load steel, which will come at 10.00
- Provide steel sheeting for crane's pads
- Get bough of tree lopped so crane can get through
- Book access plant requested by erectors to be on site the evening before they come
- Back-up required:
  Jim

My jobs as Project Manager

- Check ZZ crane hire day before
- Chase hire company day before for scissors lift
- Check insurance
- Warn neighbours to move car
- Tell lads to park elsewhere for the day (to get crane in)

Keeping supplies flowing

Given that your main subbies are all working well, and you're getting good at sequencing, it's not too hard to dovetail their work schedules so they don't get under one another's feet. Problems can arise, however, when supplying fittings and materials to these people. This is a vital part of being a good project manager as hold-ups on materials can demolish the best-laid time-line planning.

There are many ways of organising this. I tend to look at 'global' categories (doors, windows, etc) in one way – as they affect every room in the place, and one-off issues (such as the fireplace for a bedroom), in another. Items in the first group have to be organised and delivered as a piece because they come from one supplier, whereas the second group of tasks can be organised room by room. You'll find a way of achieving this that suits you best. However you do it, though, be sure you have a note of lead time and delivery date for each item. Pricing is also sensible as it keeps your feet on the ground. For example, although it would be nice to have everything as you'd like it the day you move in, maybe getting the antique dresser (see below) looking great can wait until you see how your budget goes. If it's important because it's the only clothes storage you're going to have in your bedroom, then maybe you'll look at it as part of the build and price it in as essential.

The general principle is that making sure your men have what they need to do the work will all be more predictable if you:

- Use local suppliers
- Build up loyalty with these suppliers
- Keep to standard (available from stock) items
- Keep to standard sizes and colours
- Order well ahead of time
- Pick up anything you can yourself
- Have sufficient storage to be able to buy ahead (you can also benefit from sales and special offers like this too)
- Listen to your subbies (who may have good connections and sources who won't let them down)

Attending to all the details of every phase of your build is hard work but fun. It's perfectly possible to do everything on paper or on spreadsheets if you like. If you feel like it, you could use a software programme such as Microsoft Project to create a more complete time-line of the key, time-sensitive tasks than the simple one above. It will almost certainly be unnecessary but you might enjoy doing it. And this is no bad thing since your build should be enjoyable.

Critical supplies for Master Bedroom

Item	Order by (date)	Delivery date	Price
Built-in wardrobes (W by WWW)			
Centre light fitting (Z by ZZZ)			
Fire surround			
Special lighting over dressing table			
New bed			
Carpet			
Curtains			
Refurbishing Granny's antique dresser			

PART TWO

RUNNING YOUR SITE

Introduction

Most of us who take on any sort of building project tend to see ourselves as do-ers. We fancy ourselves as hands-on practitioners and think that only office workers and civil servants sit down shifting paper, and planning all day. In fact, in my experience, many people setting out to do their own build, especially when employing a contractor, see administrative tasks and pre-planning as a waste of time, or even a bit 'wet'.

If this is what you think....I've got news for you.

For every hour you spend planning, you'll save three or four later. We've already seen how this applies to financial planning and everything involved in getting the project off the ground in the first place but it's even more vital now you're on site, as thoughtlessness, laziness, arrogance or ignorance can start to cost you real money, waste time, and make life pretty unpleasant, or even dangerous.

In this part of the book I look at the various things about your build, be it for a new house or other work, that'll need to be planned in some detail before you start to construct anything and at those tasks that'll have to be managed day by day. Many readers who've never been here will recoil at this formidable list...but those who've built before will know that this is where they'll need all their skills to pull off a successful and enjoyable project.

Once you've been through this section, draw a to-scale sketch of your site and start planning where everything will physically go. Think through exactly how you'll use materials, gain access to everything, and keep the place safe and secure. You should then be able to 'live' on your site in your mind's eye, long before you actually start to build anything. You'll be amazed how much confidence this gives you, as the manager of your project. Incidentally, but importantly, it gives others confidence, too. And this is essential if you're a novice builder.

I'm assuming in this section of the book that you're doing most of the work yourself, although you'll probably be using direct labour a lot. If you use a main contractor, much of this 'site/build management' detail will be his responsibility. However, as the project manager it's your task to be sure he does what he should, and that as the overall boss of the build and future home-owner, you are happy. Knowing what's in this part of the book is thus vital for you to be able to manage your project.

15 Neighbours

I looked on page 30 at the importance of keeping on the good side of your neighbours in the early stages of planning your build. But if you thought that was important, imagine how much more care you'll need to take once you start erecting scaffolding on their garden, streaking the road with mud, putting their cars at risk with delivery lorries, removing trees, and so on.

In the week or two before you start doing anything on site, talk (or more importantly – listen) to your immediate neighbours and any others who might be affected. By definition your building work will inconvenience them to some extent but most people, if kept informed, are pretty reasonable and will try to meet you halfway on most issues. Bear in mind they might want you to be as helpful to them one day! And, if you're doing good work it'll enhance the area generally which will, in turn, make their property more valuable.

Things that upset neighbours include:

- Being kept in the dark.....fertile imaginations make for bad enemies
- Nasty surprises
- Noise
- Anything that encroaches on their land
- Damage to their property
- Danger to their children
- Parking outside their place
- Early starts and finishes and Sunday working
- Damage to any of their underground structures (drains, foundations, gas or water supplies)
- Your site becoming a magnet for vandals
- Their feeling they have some sort of moral duty to take care of your site when you're not there

There are many more.

Before you talk to neighbours about anything practical about your build, get to grips with this chapter. If, for example, they are worried that your men will pop into their garden to relieve themselves, your plans for hiring an on-site loo will completely put their minds at rest. The more professional you appear, and the more answers you have, the less they'll worry. And this is exactly what you want. Some even quite decent people will see it as their civic duty, let alone their personal need, to ensure that you are doing what you should. For example, every tree you remove could inflame a local tree-hugger who could then hold you up while the tree preservation issue is sorted out. And so it goes on. Some neighbours will begrudge you your home improvement, and others will simply have too much time on their hands and will want to use it to police your efforts!

Do your very best to get the neighbours on your side. Make certain they know you'll be covered by insurance and that you'll make good damage done to their place. Even promise to compensate them financially for any inconvenience, if it comes to it. But don't leave things there. From time to time go out of your way to talk with them and get their feedback. I always try, periodically, to ascertain how things are going from the neighbour's point of view and to seek their input. Many's the time I've had helpful suggestions from neighbours. Sometimes things I've not even dared ask for (such as using their driveway to store something for a day) have been volunteered. Some neighbours will actually delight in your project, getting vicarious pleasure from your work...and even more delight from the fact that it isn't them doing it!

Your build....as seen from your neighbour's garden

16 Site layout

This is one of the jobs I most enjoy. It involves things that are hard for a first-timer but it's a great game of mental chess that also ensures you'll learn how to run a professional, quality build. Much of this section looks at the site from the point of view of building a new house. However, even a substantial extension or renovation project in which you live while work goes on around you, is still a building site, and most of the topics I look at here will apply every bit as much.

Start to imagine your build step by step and work through exactly what'll happen week by week. Successful builders do this almost instinctively because they've learned from experience that to fail to do so costs big money, causes delays and, in extremes, can even land them in court.

Let's look at things that will have to be planned for when starting up your site. They all need a physical presence on the site and will certainly require a mental presence in your planning. Nothing here can be avoided or ignored unless you want trouble.

Parking

Unless you have a huge site, parking and areas for taking deliveries need to be considered right from the start. The worst job I ran (from this point of view) was in a city centre where my first port of call each morning – at 07.30 – was to the local council offices to obtain parking permits for all the men...in an area that was otherwise residents-only parking. There's nothing like a few parking tickets to persuade your plumber he'd be happier working somewhere else!

This is, of course, an extreme, but we all have to calculate how many cars, vans and trucks will need a home. If you haven't built before, the numbers of vehicles coming and going will shock you.

Bear in mind that neighbours won't thank you if vans are parked outside their place (perhaps obstructing their access) for many months. Think about trades sharing vans on days they don't need to bring in materials or large tools. If you're expecting a huge truck, ask your neighbour if they'd agree to parking their own car somewhere else that day, so as to leave you room. They'll probably be pleased to co-operate when they realise that the alternative might be some less-than-careful driver nudging their prized possession in his haste to get the job done!

Deliveries are always best carried out on your land if at all possible. Make sure there's enough room for a reasonable-sized truck to turn, and be certain there's someone on hand to help them reverse in or out on to a public road. Really large artics will have to stay on the road and their loads manhandled or even craned, off. When thinking about vehicles, plan for enough safe ground for them to rest on. An early task on any new build is to ensure you have enough hard standing for vehicles. The ready-mix company will give you hell if their truck is bogged down at your place when it should be earning them money on two other deliveries that day. It'll also hold you up terribly. It may be possible to make this access road or parking area from rubble you've saved from your demolition but hardcore may have to be bought in.....painful though this might seem.

Either way, it's not something you can skimp on. No one in their busy life has time to spend getting their vehicle out of mud or cleaning themselves up after stepping in to a puddle. This is one sure way of putting people off your site.

And this is absolutely what you do not want.

Once you start planning your site it's important to sort out where vital services will go

Fencing

Depending on the nature of your site, you'll need some fencing. This both delineates the extent of your place and gives some security (see below). At the very least you'll have to hire some lightweight steel fencing that will dissuade passers-by from entering. The most common type consists of 2m high panels that have legs made to sit into heavy concrete or rubber 'shoes'. The panels link together with strong clamps.

If your build is going to take a long time, you may think it sensible to install some proper solid fencing. This usually involves timber uprights set into concrete with plywood hoardings between and a lockable gate. This keeps out all but the most determined intruder and also prevents people looking in to see what there is they could steal.

Just how much of the perimeter of your site you think advisable to protect in this way is up to you. Discuss the matter with your contractor, if you're using one.

Protecting trees, flower beds and hedges

If you have trees that are protected by a tree preservation order, place some stout stakes in the ground close by and run high-viz tape or a fence around them so they don't get damaged. Similarly, valuable flower borders or other areas of the garden you don't want hurt should be marked off somehow with temporary, easily visible, barriers.

Mains water and electricity

It makes sense to start thinking about your supplies as soon as you own the land. Arranging for connections can take up to 12 weeks to organise, so allow lots of time. Once you start planning your site it's important to sort out where these vital services will go. The temporary water stand-pipe ideally needs to go close to your sand pile and mixer. Make sure the supply pipe can't be run over by vehicles. If you ever get stuck for electricity it's possible to hire (or preferably buy) a small generator to provide the juice you need early on.

The temporary electricity supply can be placed anywhere that suits. Be sure your electrician gives you the 110v outputs you need from this board. There should be no 240v supply to a building site until the electrics in the house are properly completed by your electrician.

Lavatory

If you are doing an extension or a refurb it might be possible for your men to use an existing toilet in the house. However, this can be less than ideal as: workmen tramp muck through the place however careful they are; you feel your space is invaded; you worry about security; and few builders will be as careful as you'd like them to be with your loo. If at all possible hire a portable loo. This is essential on a new-build.

Your portable loo will have to be connected to a mains water source and the main drain (or you'll have to pay...and have the access... to have it regularly emptied by a truck).

It should, ideally, be placed somewhere at the back of the site, but close enough to mains water and sewerage. Pipes need lagging so they don't freeze in the winter.

Waste disposal

If you're in for a surprise on vehicle movements on your site, you'll be incredulous at the amount of rubbish you generate. Because it all has to be taken away, it's vital to plan how this will be achieved without causing disruption to your build.

Things that will need to be removed from your site include demolition materials; soil taken out during the foundation dig (if you don't have room to accommodate it on site for later use); stuff you clear off the site (such as old sheds, trees and other vegetation); and the waste generated at every stage of the build processes. It is now no longer acceptable to have bonfires burning all the time, as it was when I first started. It is also unwise to bury waste, even if you have a large area of land. In reality, all waste has to be taken away from the site and disposed of in a legal way.

For most of us this means using skips.

Skips are hired out by companies in various sizes. If you are going to be barrowing soil into one, be sure it has a flap-down door at one end. The skip company will deliver an empty one to you (often at some ungodly hour and with the greatest possible noise) and pick it up when you tell them it's full. When doing your costings, allow for having a skip on site the whole time. If this is impossible for some reason, then stockpile waste safely and load the skip when it comes. This obviously involves double-handling, which is costly and thus to be avoided. Such piled-up waste also gets wet, heavier and more unpleasant to handle if left lying around. It can also be dangerous. Take this route only if you have absolutely no alternative.

If at all possible, stand the skip on your own land. If it can only go on the public road you'll need a local authority permit. The cost of this is usually included in the skip hire charge (which is surprisingly high, to take into account the taxes the company has to pay for dumping in legal landfill sites). Any skip left on a public road must have lights. The skip company will tell you how to get these. If you don't have lights and something happens, your insurance company may not pay up. Some councils insist on your having a permit to take your skip over their pavement.

Skips may be all very fine but they have drawbacks. The main one is that other people will use yours to dump their stuff. Tying a strong tarpaulin over the top securely is one way around this but the really determined skip-jacker will always get through. Another drawback is that most skip companies insist on level-loading. What all their customers want, of course, is an elastic skip that takes twice the volume it was meant to! Provided your waste is secure and not too much higher than the sides, most drivers will take it away, albeit with some mutterings. Sometimes the driver will unload the excess waste (especially if you aren't around) and leave it on your site, or even on the roadside, rather than get into trouble himself. This is obviously something you should avoid. Use the same company for all your skips and get to know what they'll tolerate. Bear in mind that they have to abide by the law and can't overload skips illegally just to please you or keep your custom.

I nearly wept as truck after truck full of air left my site....along with a few sheets of concrete!

When working in built-up areas you may need to place your skip outside your house or site on the road. This could mean putting notes on cars that would otherwise be parked there, or even posting notes through the neighbours' letter boxes. Park your own car in the spare spot until the skip arrives. Cones may or may not be effective, depending on your neighbourhood.

If you plan to have a skip on your driveway during the build, a few things are worth thinking about in advance. A skip is a very large and immovable object. Be sure to place it so everyone else can get around it. Make sure there's a purpose-built crossover between road and driveway or you'll have a huge bill from the council for repairing their pavement, and possibly even underlying structures too. Make certain your own driveway can cope with such a heavy truck and its hydraulic legs. Always put substantial timbers under the legs to spread the load when the skip is moved. There are no prizes for damaging your own drive surface, drains, manholes and so on. Large sheets of shuttering ply should be placed where the lorry's wheels will go, in addition to substantial load-bearing timbers for the legs to sit on.

Obviously, salvaging valuable items can generate actual cash

When loading a skip you might want to cover adjacent vehicles with a stout cloth or tarpaulin so that dust and small debris don't damage them. If the car isn't yours, get permission first. If a car does get covered with dust, hose it down rather than trying to remove debris in any other way. If you need to get the council to suspend a parking bay for your skip to sit there, be prepared for them to charge you for lost revenue!

Muck-away lorries are large trucks that remove big volumes of various materials from your site. This usually means earth taken out during the excavation of the foundations, though demolition can produce large volumes too. When trying to calculate the numbers of lorries you'll need, bear in mind that your soil has been compacted over millions of years. Once disturbed it will bulk up alarmingly as air becomes incorporated into the mix. The exact multiplier of original volume in the ground to the volume that leaves your site varies according to soil type but can be as much as three times the hole in the ground! My worst muck-away job involved taking down a concrete building, surrounded by massive concrete roadways. I nearly wept as truck after truck full of air left my site....along with a few sheets of concrete! Short of crushing the concrete on site there was simply no way round this.

A variation on these trucks is a grab lorry. These, as the name suggests, have a hydraulic arm and an operator who can grab the waste and load it directly into the truck. Although this means stockpiling, it can often be a good and speedy option where you can't get a skip in.

Today, we are all more conscious of recycling but here it's worth mentioning that your local authority may have contacts for recycling various things. If you end up with lots of one particular type of waste (hardcore, timber or soil, for example), you could find that a supplier will collect it for nothing because they can sell it on to someone else. Obviously, salvaging valuable items can generate actual cash.

Materials storage

Whoever supplies you with materials, and whether you're building yourself, or employing a contractor, materials will all need a home.

The materials for your build could amount to 50 per cent of the total building budget, so they'll need looking after at every stage.

Let's look at the main materials in turn.

Sand, cement and plaster. Although sand might appear to be a pretty robust substance, this isn't actually the case. A pile of sand can: freeze in the winter, thus delaying progress for that day; easily get contaminated with debris, if not protected; get soaking wet, thus making it difficult for brickies to use; lose its 'fines' (the very smallest particles that give it 'fluidity'); and soon be washed away into the surrounding land. Think carefully where to put your sand pile as it cannot easily be moved. It needs to be close enough to the action but in no one's way. There must also be good access for when it needs topping up.

> **Think carefully where to put your sand pile as it cannot easily be moved. It needs to be close enough to the action but in no one's way**

Cement is terribly water-sensitive. Admittedly, it comes in bags that have a plastic inter-lining but this by no means makes them water-proof. Even slightly damp cement is completely unusable. It must be stored in a dry, well-ventilated place. The same applies to plaster, though this is even more likely to get damaged by water, even from the atmosphere. In general, it's best to get supplies of cement and plaster regularly in small doses rather than stock-piling them. Cement and plaster both have a limited shelf life. Be guided by the date stamp on the bag.

Bricks and blocks. These must be kept covered, or they'll get wet and be hell to lay. It might at first appear that a brick is a robust waterproofing surface to a wall but in reality it can soak up a lot of water, making laying tricky as mortar runs down the face, staining the brick, perhaps permanently. Very wet bricks are also heavier to handle. Concrete blocks soak up lots of water and can be seriously heavy to use when drenched. Both wet bricks and wet blocks also reduce the quality of the bond that occurs between them and their securing mortar. The final, dried-out colour of the mortar can also end up patchy, according to the wetness of the masonry at the time of laying.

All this means that bricks and blocks should be covered on site at all times.

Bricks and blocks usually come to site in stacks on pallets. These pallets need to be placed with some thought as they can't be moved easily. If at all possible get the people who deliver them to place the stacks as close as possible to where you want to use them. Taking bricks and blocks around a site is time-consuming and expensive. I try whenever possible to get the driver to place my blocks exactly where I need them using the long hydraulic arm on the back of the lorry. If you're doing a second floor, the driver can place stacks of blocks on large, strong boards directly on the floor joists, so no one has to carry them up.

Carrying bricks and blocks around a site is not only tedious but opens you up to all kinds of damage. Carelessly throwing bricks into a barrow will chip them, especially if they're a soft type. Blocks too can sustain damage, which will matter if they are going to have their 'fair face' showing in the final building. A broken block also has less structural strength.

Brickwork and block work should ideally be covered, once laid, until the mortar has 'gone off' (bonded one unit of masonry to another), or anyway if there's frost or strong sun about. Both frost and sun can aversely affect the strength of the bond, making the completed masonry structure weaker than it should be.

Plasterboard and chipboard. Plasterboard needs to be stored indoors or at the very least under cover. It's extremely sensitive to warping when damp and wastage can be high. Plasterboard should be stored upright, against a rigid timber backing so it doesn't bow, and on battens so it doesn't rest directly on the floor. Once deformed, plasterboard cannot be used.

Chipboard too absorbs water (unless you are using the moisture proof version....which I advise) and can soon be rendered completely useless. It must be stored flat on battens indoors, or in a shed or garage.

Timber. There's a lot of timber in any build and it's an expensive material to waste. Timber absorbs moisture from damp air as well as actual rain, causing it to swell, twist, and even deteriorate completely. Once installed and drying out, wet timber can move much more than you'd imagine, even sometimes cracking walls. Timber exposed to the sun can crack or warp. The best way to store timber is flat, in a stack, with battens separating the layers, so air can percolate. The stack should be well covered at all times.

If you have bought tanalised timber (impregnated with preservative), it can be very wet if the process has been performed recently. Let it dry out well before use.

Prepared timber for skirting, architraves and so on should always be stored indoors as it is usually so much thinner in section than structural timbers and thus subject to warping with moisture or temperature changes.

Store your timber in a way that's obvious according to its final use. It's all too easy for a chippie to get confused and used the wrong timbers, perhaps cutting a small piece from each of several lengths to fit a particular situation when you'd got it that length especially so it would do another job, uncut. This can be a painfully expensive error but the chances it'll occur can be minimized by stacking similarly-dimensioned timbers in the same place.

Valuable items. So far I've considered only so-called 'heavy side' building materials (large-volume, relatively inexpensive stuff) but over the duration of your build you'll need to store all kinds of quite small and valuable items such as your kitchen.

There are many ways to deal with this. You can hire a lockable, steel storage cabin; build your garage first and use this as a secure store; or keep things in your existing home (or somewhere else on the site if it's a refurb or conversion). You can then bring them over as required. The best rule of thumb is to have valuable materials and fittings on site for the shortest time possible before installation.

17 Hiring plant

If you are running your own build you'll definitely be hiring plant at some stage. If you employ a builder, he'll hire what's needed but will need somewhere secure to store things. Most sub-contractors supply their own plant and hand tools but if several trades need something special, for example a scissors lift, then it's worth your hiring it and letting each one use it, provided, of course, they have the required training and certification to do so.

You can hire plant of every conceivable description from local companies, national chains, and even some builders' merchants. It can be a real dilemma whether to buy a particular item or rent it. Some self-builders buy second-hand from other self-builders, then sell on again at the end.

In general, the first 24 hours' hire is really expensive. Subsequent days get cheaper and hiring by the week or month is cheapest of all. By about ten or twelve weeks you'll have paid for the cost of the item you're hiring, so hiring clearly makes sense only for short periods. Whether you hire or buy, about two per cent of your total build budget will go on hiring plant or buying tools. If you intend to do lots of projects then buying is definitely the way to go. If this is a one-off, or you're employing a main contractor, then hire what you need, as you need it. If you're hiring a lot of stuff from one source, get them to open an account for you. Setting up an account with a local outfit means you'll get a discount. It'll also be beneficial because you won't have to worry about paying when you pick things up or have them delivered. Keep a close eye on your dockets to be sure you receive the agreed discount and that the actual hire period is what you're charged for. This has all the advantages of having an account with a builders' merchant (see page 168).

By about ten or twelve weeks you'll have paid for the cost of the item you're hiring, so hiring clearly makes sense only for short periods

Most plant hire companies can supply what you want within a few days, often the same day. If you plan ahead you can book what you need so you know it'll be there. Plan ahead with your subbies what they'll need and when. Most hire companies will deliver and collect their property for a small charge, which is handy, especially for heavy items. Obviously, large plant must come on a trailer or truck.

When you've finished with something, call the hire company so it can go 'off hire', and you won't be charged for it any more. No matter if they can't get to collect it for some days, you won't be paying. It will, however, still be your responsibility insurance-wise because it's on your site. Make sure items go back clean and complete or you'll end up paying.

The responsibilities of hire companies today are considerable. They must ensure that the item is in good, safe, tested working order; and must instruct you how to use it if they have any doubts at all. You, in turn, will have to use the item in the way it is intended to be used and must insure it and keep it safe. When hiring large equipment you may need to sign something to show that you understand the responsibilities you are undertaking. It's up to you as boss to ensure that anyone using such equipment is properly trained and has the required certificates to prove it. No one should ever use hired equipment without your permission.

For small builds the hire company will offer you insurance cover.

Scaffolding is a rather specialised area of plant hire. It is used mainly for roofing and for access to upper storeys. Scaffolding companies hire out materials for a fixed period of time for an agreed sum. Roofers either have their own scaffolding, or hire it and then charge you. A standard house might need scaffolding for 10 weeks, with a surcharge if you keep it for longer than this. Scaffolding needs adjusting and extending as the build progresses. Your scaffolders' quote will take this extra work into account.

Tell them you'll need ladders as required. And be sure they supply all the safety handrails etc required, in the price.

If you are thinking of hiring your own scaffolding you'll need to give the companies you ask to tender the following information:

- A complete set of drawings
- The number of 'lifts' that will be required (a standard, two-storey house will need four lifts...raises of the scaffold's level)
- The length of time you'll need it
- Any special requirements

If you take responsibility for your own scaffolding, be sure to keep in close touch with the brickies so you can tell the scaffolders when to come back to lift the scaffold to the next level. They'll usually need a few days' notice. Get all levels cleared of materials so when they arrive they won't have to wait around. Some won't be prepared to wait and those that do will charge you.

If your job is small enough it's possible to hire other types of scaffold that slot together rather like a sturdy tower. This can be done by trained operatives who aren't scaffolders. Your builders may be able to use this system, providing you with considerable flexibility compared with formal scaffolding.

18 Security

It's a sad fact that theft from building sites is common. All of us who've run sites have lost power tools and small pieces of plant. Unfortunately, it's also possible to 'lose' very large plant. Most modern motorised plant is fitted with immobilisers.

Early on in your build you'll be using materials that are heavy and of relatively low unit value but as things progress, items generally get smaller (and thus more easily stolen) and more valuable.

If the worst comes to the worst, your insurance (see page 74) will cover any theft you suffer but the inconvenience and loss of building time can be substantial while all this is sorted out.

Prevention is the best medicine here.

Ways of reducing theft:

- A good perimeter fence will help if you're in a dense city or high-crime area. When thinking about fencing for security, remember it has a second function too – deterring outsiders who might later sue you if they come to harm while trespassing. You only have to have one experience like this in a lifetime to make a fence seem good value!
- Installing lighting that's activated by movement sensors. This can be a nuisance to neighbours if animals or tree foliage movement sets them off
- Installing a webcam you can access from your home computer
- Keeping the amount of valuable materials on site to a minimum....ideally bringing them in just before installation
- Hiring or buying a lockable steel cabin/container for valuables
- Taking power tools and small, valuable items home with you each night
- Hiding mixers and other plant out of sight so they aren't too obvious to opportunistic passers-by
- I usually build my garage first if I can (much to everyone's consternation!) and then use this as a secure lock-up. You don't need to install the expensive final garage doors: simply make the door openings safe with timber and ply boards, then use the passenger door
- Getting the house itself glazed and with lockable doors as soon as you can
- In a remote location it can make sense to employ a security company to call by out of working hours. If you go this route, display their company sign prominently as a deterrent
- Scaffolding can be fitted with alarms that are triggered if people try to climb it
- Remove all ladders at the end of the working day that give access to upper floors – or otherwise render the ladders un-climbable. If the place is scaffolded be sure that upstairs windows are kept shut
- Use large plant to trap smaller items, or chain small things to the big stuff

Site rules and discipline

Building sites, like all places of work, need at least some rules. As manager of your build you must decide what these rules will be.

Site discipline can be a tricky issue when dealing with temporary employees, some of whom may not have your ideas of what a build

Be disciplined about site dress code

Things to consider include:

- Smoking. The site should be non-smoking but there should be a smoking area
- Radios. If you're happy with these, then discuss reasonable volume
- Parking. Be clear about who may and may not park on site, and where
- Clearing waste as it is produced. Say who is responsible for this
- Dress code. Say if you want or need people to wear high-visibility ('high-viz') clothing
- Safety equipment. Make it clear that this should be used, and show everyone where it's kept. Hard hats and safety footwear should be standard
- Alcohol. No alcohol or drugs allowed at any time
- Tool voltage. Only 110v tools to be brought on site
- Conduct generally. To be good and courteous at all times
- Use of toilet. To be agreed if in an existing premises, or site loo if on a new build
- Emergency access. No cars or vans to obstruct the site entrance

should be, and some of whom may not be very disciplined individuals at the best of times. If you have reason to be unhappy with someone's behaviour, be careful and courteous about how you tell them. You may find you'll have an argument on your hands if the individual feels aggrieved or picked on. Try to keep everything calm and enlist the assistance of an older, experienced hand from the workers to help keep matters cool.

If a subbie is clearly not doing things the way you want, ask him to see you privately for a talk. Tell him why you're unhappy and see what he intends to do to remedy matters. Warn him that you want to see change. If things persist, give him a warning in writing. If matters are still no better, get rid of him. If you are drawing up a labour-only contract with someone it's vital right from the start to plan for how such a dismissal will take place.

The sorts of things you'll be watching out for (and may need to get rid of someone for) include:

- Poor time-keeping
- Ignoring Health and Safety issues
- Flaunting the site rules
- Poor quality workmanship
- Poor output
- Drinking or taking drugs on site
- Rudeness or discourtesy to others (especially visitors)
- Using tools/plant improperly
- Theft
- Poor attitude

20 Health, safety and welfare

Before you slope off to sit muttering in a dark corner, let's talk about the good news. As a self-builder you are not governed by the Health and Safety at Work Act 1974. And if you employ a main contractor, he has to worry about all this.

However, life isn't that simple. First of all, whatever the Law says, you have a moral duty to look after the health, safety and welfare of your workforce, visitors and neighbours, any of whom could take legal action against you. Anyone who comes into contact with your project has a right, under health and safety legislation, to be protected from danger.

We live in an increasingly litigious world and some people, especially when vexed or bitter, will hit out at those around them.

If someone is injured on your site due to your negligence or ignorance of the law, you could be sued.

This means that whether you are building yourself or employing a main contractor you, as the overall manager of the project, have to ensure that everything is being done as it should.

Building sites are very dangerous places. I always remind people that their building site is in reality a factory, run out of doors, on a one-off basis just to produce their house, and without the benefit of factory-like health and safety controls. I know it's not what you'll want to hear but safety today can cost more than the cost of materials and labour in certain building processes. People may not, for example, perch on ladders installing heavy windows to the first floor (hire a scissors platform); or install guttering off ladders (use a tower). It's your duty to be aware of and to pre-think all the safety issues in advance of any work being done.

This thinking ahead, task by task, comes with experience but if you're new to the business, or in any doubt, invaluable guidelines as to best practice are available from the Health and Safety Executive helpline on 0845 3450055 or their website: www.hse.gov.uk. As you'd expect, in todays complex world, there are rules and regulations governing every conceivable aspect of construction, so I cannot hope to list them here.

It can be tempting to cut corners but it's foolish to do so. Not only could you be asking your men to put their lives or health at risk but you'll get a worse job done. Research shows that on sites where health and safety issues are well managed the quality of work is always higher. This is hardly too surprising when you think about it.

I know many readers will by now be thinking, 'None of this is likely to happen to me'. But

Main hazard areas to be aware of include:

- Anything to do with electricity. Keep an eye open for cables being driven over, frayed or cut. Long extension leads should be avoided if at all possible. Use only 110v tools. Accidents involving electricity commonly kill
- Falling from a height or being hit by a vehicle are other common causes of death. I have personally had two near-death experiences with vehicles reversing into me. It is very hard indeed for operatives to watch every possible angle, especially behind them and when concentrating on the job in hand. In my view the responsibility for an individual's safety in this regard lies with him and he should keep his eyes and ears open when anywhere near motorised plant
- Handling, lifting or carrying can easily cause injury. Back injuries are terribly common among builders
- Inexperienced workers (those in the first six months of their employment) provably have more accidents than others. Take special care of new and inexperienced workers
- Excavations. Once a trench is deeper than waist height there is a danger of collapse. Excavations are dangerous because they are, by definition, below ground and thus hard to see. Trenches must be shored up with timbers and the area marked clearly as a hazard. In general, try to get trenches filled in as quickly as possible. Holes in the ground are a disaster waiting to happen
- Concrete can be very dangerous. Those without experience don't realise how terribly corrosive it is to skin and eyes. Make sure that concrete doesn't splash during placement. If it gets in your eye, wash with lots of plain water at once and, if in doubt, seek medical advice. Wear stout Wellington boots during placement
- Clear up timbers with nails in them or they'll go through someone's foot
- Conversion work. New-builds are much more controllable and thus safer than refurbs or conversions. Taking out old walls and modifying existing (often unpredictable) structures is dangerous and needs huge care. There may also be an asbestos hazard and poisonous fumes when lead-based paints are stripped with a hot air gun. The potential for danger on conversion work is always higher than with new work

they'd be wrong. If we run a building site, or cause it to be run on our behalf, we have moral, legal and economic reasons for getting all this right.

I need hardly spell out the moral angles. Whoever is at fault, it is hell when someone is seriously injured on your site....let alone killed. When something adverse occurs to a visitor or a local, inquisitive child, things are even worse. At least a construction worker knows what he's in for when choosing to work in the industry.

I've looked briefly at the legal implications. But if something dreadful were to happen your site could be closed down and you'd be at risk of legal action, too. None of this bears thinking about in the small hours, so it pays to be responsible at every level.

The financial implications of closing your site; of higher insurance premiums; and even perhaps of having to re-employ a new workforce, are also considerable. According to one expert, for every £1 of known and obvious cost, hidden costs can amount to anything from £8-£36 when taking into account: the interruption of your build; replacement staff pay (people always cost more when you need them in a crisis); damage to property, plant and equipment; loss of a good worker; retraining a new one; legal and other professional costs; and fines.

So much for safety. Now to health.

Many procedures and processes in the construction industry involve things that can damage someone's health. It's your job to ensure that by pre-thinking every stage you don't put anyone's health at risk. This means, not only considering your own actions but those of others.

The welfare of your workforce may not seem very glamorous but it makes a huge difference to the realities of running a site day after day. A man who feels cared for works better.

At the most basic level you must supply your men with a clean source of running water, a place to rest, somewhere to change, and a working loo. None of this needs to be flashy but it needs to be there.

Thinking about more complex areas of welfare, give careful consideration to the following:

- Be very aware how things are stacked and stored. Check each day that piles of materials are still stable and safe
- Keep a careful eye on all plant to be sure it's in a safe condition
- Look out for things that could fall from a height. Ensure kick boards on scaffolds are securely in place
- Check around every day to be sure that no one has modified a scaffold or other safety feature. Workers have a habit of taking out things that are in their way, then forgetting to replace them
- Check frequently that the lighting is adequate, the men aren't working in the cold, and ventilation is appropriate if chemicals are being used, or high levels of dust produced. Trips and falls occur much more commonly when these sorts of welfare issues are ignored
- Be aware of the heath and safety of outsiders. For example, if you have a deep excavation, all your men will know about it but you must still erect a suitable notice in case others come onto the site who do not know. Some of these might even be trespassers...but you still have to protect them
- Have you got a first aid box somewhere everyone on the site knows about? If you're running a big job, do you have someone who is trained in first aid? Does everyone know who he is?

Look after your men's welfare

When instructing anyone to do anything you need to ask yourself:

- Are they capable of doing it? Do they have the required skills/training? If you're not certain, ask and, if necessary, get someone else to do the task
- Are they physically capable of the task? If you know someone has a back problem, be careful about what you ask them to lift
- Have you provided them with the correct personal protective equipment (PPE) to do the job? You'll need to have hard hats, rubber gloves, heavy duty gloves, eye protection, ear plugs and protectors, masks, knee protectors, fire-resistant trousers (for welding), Wellington boots, and high-viz jackets available at all times and in a location of which everyone is aware. It'll be your responsibility to ensure that these items are always readily available, not left around the site
- Have you made sure that people working around an operative are safe from their actions? For example, don't have someone welding close to others who are not protected
- Consider whether you should be employing specialist contractors rather than asking your men to do things that are outside their competence, just to save money. You might well, in fact, save money because the specialists could do it in half the time and at no risk. As you'll have seen from reading this far, I'm a fan of specialists. They might cost more but they know exactly what they're doing; usually get the job done faster; take responsibility for their own tools and plant; know what the heath and safety hazards are; often have specific insurance cover; and free up your men to do what they are best at

Ideally, you should also provide a place for the men to eat. On small, domestic sites this has to be improvised but there has to be somewhere.

It's clear that to make a site totally safe and to take the welfare of your workers into consideration could cost a lot. On domestic building sites the standards are nowhere near as high as they are on commercial sites. This is expected and, to some extent, allowed for in the legislation. Even if you are very careful you won't be able to engineer out all risks to the health, safety and welfare of your men.

However, you can, in law, reasonably be expected to have made serious efforts to control the risks involved.

So far I've concentrated on your responsibilities as the employer/manager. But of course this legislation cuts both ways. Employees too have obligations while on your site. They are expected to take reasonable care of themselves; to be aware of risks they may be causing others; to do what is asked by their employer to reduce risks both to themselves and others; and not to interfere with anything in a way that makes the site more dangerous. In theory, an employee could be prosecuted for his own injuries. Your men also have a duty to report dangers or hazards to you or the main contractor.

Construction (Design and Management) Regulations (CDM Regs) came into force in 1994. These new rules made it necessary to organise heath and safety issues in a formal way with a 'Plan', created by the designer, and administered by the main contractor. If your project is your home, then CDM regs don't apply. However, if you're a developer, they do. A planning supervisor will have to be appointed and a Plan drawn up to asses all the risks likely to be encountered and details of how they'll be managed. Failure to do any of this could, in the extreme, land you in jail. Local authority building regs departments and the NHBC now offer 'planning supervision services' for a fee.

Even if you are building a private house, someone has to look out for health and safety issues. Your contractor will usually take this responsibility on board but even when I employ a contractor I still take this all very seriously. When I'm running a site I see myself as a sort of father figure to my men. I keep a constant eye out for their welfare, look out for any dangerous practices, constantly ask myself what I could do to make their life easier or safer, and so on. By caring for your men like this they'll not only feel valued but will produce better work.

If you are trying for a high-quality build you overlook health, safety and welfare at your peril. Every hour and every penny is well spent in these vital areas of running a site.

21 Keeping records

I know many readers will groan and want to skip on to somewhere else in the book at this point. I'd encourage you not to, though, because record-keeping is a vital part of both project management and running a site. I make this distinction because you'll need to have two sets of records. The former will be created from the very first day you think of doing your project but your site records will obviously not kick in until you start to run the site.

There are three main reasons for keeping good records:

- For your own interest and to learn lessons for the future
- To enable you to manage the project and run your site better
- To enable you to deal with disputes and problems more effectively

Paperwork that's important to keep:

- The first notes and sketches you did within the family while deciding whether or not to go ahead. Always fun, let alone instructive, to look back on
- A few photos of the site/property before anything was done, etc. The bulk of all your pictures will obviously be on a computer disk somewhere
- All dealings with estate agents when looking for your property. I've often made mistakes on this and regretted it later. Until you actually exchange contracts on your candidate property, keep all property details and contact coordinates of everyone you dealt with during your search. You never know who you might need, or want, to call on for a valuation or advice in the future, even if you didn't buy your eventual property through them. Even some years later I've found this useful when I've wanted to go back to agents, surveyors (on aborted properties) or whomever. I have records like this that go back twenty years. And I still refer to them, albeit rarely
- Notes from initial design meetings you had with, say, an architect to see what could be feasible on your site
- Correspondence with everyone
- First draft budgeting, and what lenders etc told you at meetings. Make notes at or immediately after all such meetings and add them to your file. Keep all the correspondence you have with them. Get

into the habit of keeping a file copy of every letter you send to anyone. It's easy to get confused once you've seen several potential lenders. Keep also your personal back-of-an-envelope budgeting notes
- The first outlines of your development (sketches, etc), even if they never came to anything
- All correspondence and notes about your design and designer, including your choosing of him. This will, eventually, become a very large part of your file
- Outline drawings for planning permission. This is a really important section of your file. There'll be many revisions and alterations to your drawings, and you'll need to be able to lay your hands on the right ones at a moment's notice. I have found it helpful to run a red line through any drawing that's been superseded by a later one, so it doesn't get used in error. Don't ever make the mistake of throwing previous drawings away. They are not only good evidence of how you've got to where you are but can also be very helpful when referring to previous versions of the design. It isn't uncommon to have to go back to certain features of a now-updated drawing. Keep all drawings in chronological order, for ease of access. These past drawings are also helpful if you ever get into conflict with your designer (see page 187)
- All invoices for absolutely everything. This should also include details of how you paid. If you open a special bank account for your build, keep the Statements here
- Your specification (see page 51). I keep several copies of this handy, ready to give out. I also keep specifications of the various sub-contracts I have in hand. It can be very useful, for example, to be able to give a plumber the electrics schedule if he needs it
- Lists of suppliers, builder's merchants, sources of unusual (perhaps reclaimed) materials, etc
- Tear sheets from magazines, design books, your mood boards (won't fit in the file) and everything you've considered on your journey thus far. Again, throw nothing away. You'll be furious when you try to get back to that radiator you'd set your heart on but can't easily source again. Keep all the samples, brochures, business cards etc you've collected at self-build and home-improvement exhibitions. These can be gold dust when you need them. You'll probably have to make separate box files/piles for this sort of stuff as it's so bulky
- Everything to do with finding your builder. All meetings notes, photos of the sites and houses they'd built that you went to see; and correspondence with potential builders. Their quotes and your responses to them will of course be vital too
- Details of all insurance quotes, and policies you actually take out. Details of warranties you decide on
- Correspondence and notes of everything to do with other professionals such as surveyors, planning consultants, accountant, solicitor, bank manager and so on. All kept within their own individual file sections
- Correspondence with the planners. Details of any meetings you have had with them at their offices, or on the site. Letters from neighbours, be they for or against your development
- Copies of work schedules, time-lines and plans

Project records

Get hold of a large lever-arch (or box) file and collect everything in separate, labelled sections as your project planning proceeds. If you have a home office you'll probably find hanging-files in a cabinet more user-friendly. I also like to create a master phone numbers list that I keep handy in the front of this file, for instant reference. This list is also on the computer, of course, ready to be updated every week or so as the project grows and more names and telephone numbers are added. On one complex project of mine this list came to more than 200 people!

When I started out building I greatly underestimated how useful such a file would be. I imagined my very effective memory would do the job. I was wrong. Much of what you'll find yourself dealing with will entail a lot of detail...and you'll be very clever indeed if you can manage to keep everything at your fingertips without paperwork, over more than a year. But as well as this it's helpful and can be vital to be able to see how decisions were made by whom and when. This is not just a good learning tool for you as a budding project manager but could help you out of a spot when disputes arise.

Keeping a site diary

Project records allow you to function effectively as the project manager, but your site diary is essential in the day-to-day management of your build.

Get a large (A4) hard-back one-day-to-view diary. You could, of course, keep these records on a laptop but in my experience a diary can more easily be thrown into the back of a car or van without coming to harm! It can be useful to have a small tape recorder too, for when you're going round the site making notes, say with your architect or building control inspector.

Some people like to use a recorder because they know their memory will let them down and they prefer this to writing lists of things on a soggy piece of paper with a biro that won't work! You can then transcribe these notes into your diary, for action.

I find it hard sometimes to remember to do my diary. It helps to get into a routine each day.

Each day the site is working you should note in your diary:

- The weather conditions. Really useful when trades later offer reasons for not doing/completing the work. Can also be helpful with insurance claims. Weather is one of the biggest time-losers on a site. It can be very helpful to have a record of why you're running late
- Who came to the site to work, including how many hours they each did, if you are employing them direct by the day or hour. Subbies on a contract price can just be noted as 'Roofers all day' for example
- Appointment times for people to visit the site. I find it's easy to forget who's coming if I'm deeply involved with a complex or interesting task. Who visited the site...especially professionals. What they did and what was agreed each party would do as a result of the visit
- Who you phoned/e-mailed, with their numbers etc
- Details of deliveries and returns
- What you ordered, from whom, and their proposed delivery date, '2,000 blocks, coming Thursday'.
- What your builder asked you to order
- Details of any complaints; from neighbours, workmen, delivery drivers ('I can't ever back into your ******* place, it's too dangerous!')
- Who you paid, for what, and how. Anyone who paid you for anything
- Disputes you had, with whom and over what
- Damage to anyone's property, (such as, 'Jim backed Fred's car into neighbour's gate post'); accidents (even minor ones); theft etc
- Your 'to do' list for the day

Everything that happens on your site will have some sort of time or financial implication, so don't let your diary go un-written.

Photography

With digital photography so available and cheap, it's wise to photograph everything on your site and concern yourself later whether or not it'll be useful. If in doubt, take a picture. If you don't already have a digital camera, or are upgrading for your build, get one with a wide-angle lens. Normal small cameras cannot take pictures of most spaces in houses as the lens isn't sufficiently wide-angled to see enough of the room.

The advantage of all this photography is:

- It's cheap and easy
- It's interesting and fun to look back on
- It's a great way of keeping stakeholders informed and interested
- You can use it to prove to your bank manager or other lender that something is actually being built!
- You can learn from past mistakes when doing future projects
- You can take masses of pictures but look only at the important or significant ones. This said, the counsel of perfection is to keep every picture you take. You never know when it'll be useful. I purge picture files at the end of each job but still keep masses of pictures for years
- You can send images electronically (by e-mail) to people who need them. This has become a miracle of modern building management. I have, on occasion, e-mailed a picture of a difficult element of a build to a surveyor, specialist supplier, or architect, to have them reply within the hour on what should be done. We then act at once on their advice. In the past I might

Keep careful records of all damage and injuries

have had to wait for days for that individual to come to the site
- To record anything that has regulatory or legal significance....especially everything to do with Building Regs; Planning; damage; accident; and so on
- To record elements of the build that have been done and are about to be covered up. This ability to have X-ray eyes benefits everyone, including all future owners of the home, who'll be able to see where you routed a cable or a drain, or how you reinforced that concrete, for example. This can save trouble and loads of money in the future
- NOTE: If you're intending to include a person in the picture, ask their permission first. I once made this mistake years ago, only to have to deal with a very angry guy who was, unbeknown to me, an illegal immigrant who didn't want his whereabouts known!

22 Tax, book-keeping and VAT

When thinking about building our own home, taxation doesn't usually feature near the top of our list of priorities. In general, when we build a place for ourselves to live in the taxation considerations are small. On selling our principle residence we don't pay Capital Gains Tax (CGT) unless it is clear that we have done the development as a business and didn't live in it for a reasonable length of time. Just how long this time is, is open to legal debate. Obviously, if you do several self-builds one after the other at close intervals – as some serial self-builders do – the Revenue will reasonably assume you have become a trader and tax you accordingly.

The only real tax issue for most of us is when we use a part of our new home for a home office, or similar, and claim tax allowances against this part while we are living there. This is all perfectly legal and done by many. However, when you come to sell you'll have to pay CGT on that proportion of the house you used as an office and for which you claimed tax allowances.

It can be sensible not to declare a proportion of your home as your workplace (and therefore not to make use of any allowances) so that when you come to sell, the whole value of your home remains untaxed if it is your principle residence. If you are intending to stay in your home for many years, then making the most of your tax allowances makes sense but if you aren't so sure, forget these tax perks and go for the no-CGT route when you sell. Of course all of this assumes there is a capital gain to be made. With self-building this is almost always the case, which is why I'm mentioning it.

VAT (Value Added Tax) is a tax on goods and services, paid at the time you buy or use them.

VAT in the UK

Partly because self-building is a substantial part of the house-building scene in the UK, there is tried-and-tested legislation that makes it possible to re-claim VAT. In the Republic of Ireland things are different. I cover these separately on page 165.

I suggest anyone who is intending to build or convert their own property should look at http://www.customs.hmrc.gov.uk where everything is well explained. It's also possible to phone the National Advice Service on 0845 010 9000 between 8.00am and 8.00 pm, Monday to Friday. As a caveat, bear in mind that anything I write here could change at any time with new legislation. Please carefully check the current position before you embark on your build.

In essence, the good news is that on completion of your project you will, as a self-

A few words of caution:

- Be sure to keep on the side of the Law throughout. Never pay cash without proper receipts for VAT. Ideally, never pay cash at all. Keep a very clear paper trail of all your expenditures on the build with credit/debit card statements and cheque book stubs that agree with bank statements
- If employing a main contractor, check his credentials and that his VAT registration number is real and up to date. You can do this by taking his name, trading details, address and VAT number and calling the Advice Line number (above). They'll check everything out for you
- Keep immaculate records of everything you spend
- Talk to your accountant about your intentions well before you start the planning and design stages – let alone before you start spending anything. He'll be happy to help you set up a simple book-keeping system that will then enable him more easily to do his work later
- Make sure you are charged the correct amount of VAT as you can claim only that VAT which is correctly charged
- Get hold of Notice 719 from the Revenue so you can see what's needed from day one

builder, be able to reclaim most of the VAT paid on materials purchased for your construction. As this can amount to many thousands of pounds (often between five and ten per cent of the total build cost as a rough rule of thumb), this is no mean perk! Given that you must make your claim within the appointed time and in the correct way, this makes forward planning vital. VAT is one area of your project's management that cannot be fudged later.

Records and receipts

I know it'll sound weird but simply work to the rule that you'll keep every receipt for absolutely everything – even if it has nothing to do with VAT. In your VAT file keep all credit notes, bills, invoices, a copy of the planning permission and a copy of the plans of the building. Sit down at the end of each day and enter things in your financial Day Book. People tease me and my Day Books but they have proved invaluable on countless occasions. Years later I've looked back at them and found useful information about suppliers, prices, VAT and so on. It's time well spent. Another added benefit is if you ever get into a financial dispute with someone. Your records of what was paid (or billed), by whom, to whom and when, can quickly come to your rescue! This Day Book can also act as a useful at-a-glance financial guide as by totalling every page you can keep a watch on the overall spend.

VAT records

VAT is charged at the current standard rate as an additional percentage on most building materials. In reality VAT is a type of purchase tax. For a VAT receipt to be of any value to you (including a hand-written one paid by cash) in your future claim it must show:

- The supplier's VAT Registration Number
- The amount of VAT that has been paid
- The quantity and nature of the goods supplied
- The price for each item
- Your name and address if the receipt has a value of more than £100

Everything must be clearly readable. If things can't be read, ask for a better copy.

When you come to make your claims at the end of the project, you'll need to supply originals, not photocopies. I suggest making copies of all receipts very soon after you get them and then keeping these separately from the originals somewhere for safe keeping (off the site). If you were to lose your stack of receipts you'd be in serious trouble. Building sites can be messy places and it's easy to throw a receipt down somewhere only to find it hopelessly faded from exposure to sunlight months later. This does you no favours!

Are all self-builders eligible for the scheme?

No. The works must be carried out in the UK (but not the Channel Islands) and the building must not have a business use. The VAT Refund Scheme is not for developers, landlords, property that is to be rented out, property that is built to be sold on immediately, B&B operators, residential home care operators or membership clubs and associations. If you work from home, though, you can still make a claim for that portion you'll use as an office.

Although it is generally thought that self-builders spend all their time personally laying tiles and pouring concrete, this isn't the case. The overwhelming majority use sub-contractors, individual tradesmen or even a single contractor for the work. This is still all allowable under the VAT refund scheme. You can also claim for the fitting out of a shell bought from a builder or developer. But you can't claim for work you do to complete a building that is already 'completed' by a developer (adding a garage, for example).

Make copies of all receipts very soon after you get them and then keep these separately from the originals

Don't forget that this refund system applies to conversions too. If a building was not originally used as a dwelling (such as an old dairy) the Refund is available if it has been unoccupied or unused for ten years or more. Recent legislation introduced a five per cent band applying to buildings empty for more than three years, and also to work involved in changing the number of living units in a building. This is all very helpful to self-builders. To prove a property has been empty for a suitable length of time before you start your work you may have to contact the Empty Property Officer at your local authority. They will write a letter confirming the place has been unoccupied for the appropriate length of time and this will back up your VAT claim. When carrying out a conversion of a non-residential building like this you can claim the VAT charged by your builder for converting the building.

Before you start to build, go to the website I mentioned above and get the necessary forms.

Builders can have different VAT ratings. A builder creating a new house for you will not charge VAT at all on his services. If he supplies goods, though, he'll charge you VAT at his appropriate rate and you'll be able to reclaim this amount.

What building materials can I claim for?
Put simply, you can claim for those that are 'incorporated' into the building itself or the site. They must be fixed and be a part of the structure such that their removal would damage the site or building.

A short list of things you can claim for:

- Outside: drainage, paths, driveways, fencing, boundary walls
- Air conditioning
- Burglar alarm
- Fitted kitchen cupboards
- Indoor swimming pool
- TV aerials
- Ventilation
- Curtain poles and rails
- Windows
- Smoke alarms
- Solar panels
- Doors
- Wooden floors
- Fireplaces
- Lifts
- Wiring
- Power sockets
- Built-in vacuum system
- Solid fuel cookers and oil-fired boilers
- Plumbing installation
- Decorating materials
- Heating system
- Light fittings
- Turf, plants and trees (if detailed on your planning documents)
- Fitted wardrobes (if a part of the house rather than a demountable kit that could be removed and used elsewhere)

You cannot claim for:

- The land itself. There should be no VAT charged on bare building land anyway. Tell the vendor you intend to build your own place. If the site has some services there could be a small amount of VAT due but it won't be on the whole value of the site
- The full VAT refund on conversions. Contractors and builders can charge a reduced VAT rate of 5% on conversions
- Granny annexes that cannot be used or disposed of separately from the main house. This is because a granny annex is not 'designed as a dwelling' from the start
- Detached workshops, playrooms or enclosed swimming pools, for the same reason as the above point
- Garden ornaments, ponds, sheds and greenhouses
- Fitted furniture
- Carpets and other floor coverings that can be removed
- Most electrical appliances
- Consumables (sandpaper, paint brushes)
- Any services. You cannot, for example, claim back VAT on the professional services of architects, surveyors, designers, planning consultants, project management etc. You also cannot claim back the VAT on hiring tools and plant, buying tools or plant, or hiring services such as skips/ladders/access/scaffolding etc
- Extensions. This makes it vital to incorporate that conservatory as soon as you possibly can on your new house build, rather than waiting a year or two after you've completed your build. If you do wait, you'll lose out on the VAT refund on the materials

Building materials bought from any EU source qualify for the VAT refund. You have to be able to supply the details of the import and evidence that the VAT has been paid. You'll also be required to submit the amount of your claim in sterling.

If you import items from non-EU countries you can still claim back the VAT but you have to prove you've paid VAT and also show copies of transit and shipping documents.

When to claim

This should be done at the completion of all the work on the project. This means completing everything that you'll ever want to claim on. This precludes leaving outside work such as the driveway until a later date (perhaps for lack of cash). You can make only one claim and that must be for everything at one hit. Get a claim pack from the Revenue or print off the forms from the website.

It can be hard to know exactly when your build is complete (see below) but it is usually common sense once everything is done according to the original planning documents. You may also get a completion certificate from your council or architect to say things are complete. If you are borrowing money this will be vital so you can get your final payment, or at the very least inform your lender that everything is complete. A letter from them can be used to inform the Revenue that things are complete. A council tax assessment can also be used.

From this completion date you now have three months to make your claim.

Send in:

- The claim form
- A description of the building goods and their quantities
- Other goods/materials and services claimed for
- Your claim calculations
- The VAT invoices and other documents that support your claim
- Evidence that the work has been completed
- A copy of the planning permission
- A copy of the plans

When making your calculations, don't forget to allow for credits or discounts given by your suppliers; returned goods or bulk purchases.

Keep a copy of everything you send just in case the Revenue comes back to you for clarification.

Your refund payment will usually come through in a further 30 days after your claim is lodged, provided the Revenue doesn't need clarification on anything.

VAT in the Republic of Ireland (ROI)

The numbers of people who actually build their own homes in the ROI is very small. True, some have them built for them by a contractor. As we shall see, in terms of VAT there's no difference.

Starting at the beginning – your land. When you buy a site the vendor cannot charge you VAT unless the site is a 'serviced' one. This type of site isn't just a virgin piece of grass but has services added, such as electricity, sewerage, roadways, fencing, and so on. The vendor can now charge you VAT but you cannot claim it back. Serviced sites can be attractive because a lot of the infrastructure work has been done by someone else but bear in mind that the added VAT will mean this all comes at a price. You'll have to take a view on what this means to you.

Now to the house itself. It is not possible to claim back any of the VAT you have paid when building your own home or having it built for you. If you use a single main contractor he will charge 13.5% and you cannot claim this back. This contractor should employ all of his own professionals and tradesmen. If he sub-contracts things out you'll end up paying more because the individual tradesman will also add his profit margin (along with accompanying VAT).

A few examples of both 'fixtures' and 'fittings'. For a more complete list go to www.revenue.ie/leaflets/vat-building.htm

'Fixtures' on which you pay VAT at 13.5%
Air conditioning
Attic insulation
Attic ladders
Baths
Built-in kitchen units
Built-in wardrobes and presses
Burglar alarm
Central heating system
Double glazing
Electrical wiring
Fencing posts
Fires escapes
Fireplaces
Floor coverings stuck down to the floor
Gates
Insulation in cavity walls
Immersion heaters
PABX telephone systems
Sewerage treatment plants
Storage heaters/radiators
Storage tanks for oil/water
Wooden floors

'Fittings' on which you pay VAT at 21%
Blinds
Curtains
Stand-alone electric and gas fires
Fitted carpet and lino
Kitchen cookers
Lighting (other than recessed lighting)
Mirrors
Shelving
Refrigerators/deep freezers
Washing machines/dishwashers etc
'Floating' wooden flooring

If you use direct labour and act as a project manager, you pay VAT for labour provided by VAT-registered tradesmen, at 13.5%. Building materials, with the exception of ready-to-pour concrete and concrete blocks (to which the 13.5% rate applies) are all changed at 21%.You cannot claim any of this back. If you were to build the entire property yourself, you still can't claim any VAT back on your materials. Specifically, there is no provision for the repayment of any excess of VAT charged at 21% on building materials over the 13.5% which would be chargeable if the work had been done by a VAT-registered Contractor.

Where the subject of VAT becomes interesting to self-builders in a jurisdiction that doesn't allow any reclaims of VAT, is the amount payable in the first place. Certain items when installed into a new house qualify for the 13.5% rate of VAT once they have been permanently installed as fixtures. Others, classified as fittings, are subject to VAT at 21%. To qualify, a 'fitting' must be able to be removed from a building without causing substantial damage to the building in its removal.

If you are intending to use part of your home as an office you can claim VAT back on these parts but, as I mentioned above in the UK section, you'll have to pay CGT when you come to sell.

Almost all self-builders will be offered goods and services for less money if they pay cash and thus save themselves VAT. This is, of course, illegal as it encourages tradesmen to avoid paying income tax that is due to the Revenue. Strictly speaking this tax avoidance is the business of the tradesman who engages in it but it is still sensible to steer clear of in case you too become implicated.

If you are about to build your own home, whether it be using a main Contractor or several sub-contractors, it makes sense to take professional advice before you even start.

23 Buying stuff

If you're managing a major self-build one thing you'll be doing lots of is shopping. Indeed, some people say this is the part they most enjoy. Spending money can, indeed, be fun.

However, it won't be spending for spending's sake and what you decide will affect your overall budget in a way you're not used to when just getting a new sitting room carpet, for example. There'll be loads of compromises to be made as you'll undoubtedly want to buy things that are too expensive for your budget. You'll have to 'rob Peter to pay Paul' all the time.

OK, you may well have bought a bathroom suite before but the chances are you'll never have been exposed to the marketplace that is the building supplies industry. This is a different world because unlike buying a new TV, prices will be negotiable and you'll have to get used to bargaining, haggling and doing deals. Unfortunately, this game is weighted against you as a novice because you simply won't able to achieve the discounts seasoned professional building companies can. This doesn't mean you won't be able to do better than someone walking in off the street but don't be disappointed when you learn what others are paying.

When buying from any source, be sure to compare not just the price but also the delivery charges and guarantees. Also check that you really are comparing like with like. Even apparently small changes in specification can make big differences to quality, performance, after-sales service, guarantee cover, and much more. Timing is also vital. While you may save something by sourcing an item yourself, if you get your timing wrong you'll hold up your contractor or the subbies and the delay could easily cost you more than you've saved. Check every day or two how your subbies are doing for materials. Get them to estimate ahead what they'll need a few days from now, in order to keep work flowing. Once you gain experience you'll be able to foresee these needs without asking anyone.

Careful buying could save you a fifth of your non-labour budget. Canny buying is obviously

Ways of sourcing things include:

- Direct from a specialist supplier
- From a builders' merchant
- On-line
- From the 'sheds' (DIY mega-stores)
- Through your builder, or other professionals
- Through (self-) building exhibitions
- At information centres (such as The Building Centre, in London: www.thebuildingcentre.co.uk)

a skill worth learning, and time worth spending! As with buying anything it's a trade-off between saving and time. If it takes you a week to find the right bathroom suite at a bargain price you'll have lost much more money than the saving is worth. It's a bit like people who drive miles to save a fraction of a penny per litre on their petrol. And although some of your buying will be fun, a lot certainly will not. There'll be many thousands spent on terribly unglamorous 'stuff' that goes into making your build work. By this I don't just mean eye-watering-budget-loads of ready-mix but supplies as unlikely as mastics, sealants, screws, hardcore for your parking, and so on! Everyone thinks of the major set-pieces (kitchens, bathrooms etc) when talking about building but the nitty-gritty of daily building work involves a lot of cash going out on pretty ordinary items. It can be especially painful when you're new to the job to fork out for things you know will be of only temporary use (site fencing, parking areas, temporary roadways, and so on).

> **If it takes you a week to find the right bathroom suite at a bargain price you'll have lost much more money than the saving is worth**

I've already said in various places that the building industry favours those who pay. This is seen in no sharper focus than in the purchasing side of a project. The better the relationships you can build with suppliers by paying them promptly and treating them well, the better your discount will be. This is obviously a chicken-and-egg situation on your first build, or when you're building in a new area but the principle still stands and is worth working towards.

When I first started out, major builders' merchants were pretty loath to engage with small fry like me. All this has changed over the years, though, with almost everyone happy to take your money if you settle their bills. There are now three major national chains in the UK; a few fair-sized regional outfits (each with several yards); a few truly independent businesses; and some DIY sheds which are supplying the trade. In addition, specialist centres for plumbing and central heating; joinery (windows, stairs, cupboards and doors); roofing and glazing offer advice and a more personal feel but usually cost more than the chains.

Opening an account

Although you might think it a big step for your first build, the first thing to do is to open accounts with the suppliers you intend to use on any scale. It won't make sense to do this for the odd tap or basin but if a company feels you're likely to spend thousands with them they'll be delighted to see you. Talk to the branch manager or the sales manager. He'll set you up with an account. This now means you can get a discount but better yet, you won't need to pay on taking goods and will, in effect, get a month's credit. Even within the large, multi-branch merchants some managers prefer not to deal with self-builders while others are delighted to do so. Check with your local one before you go in to see them. Most trade accounts need a bank reference and two trading references. If you're just starting out and can't supply trade references, write a letter to the manager and say so. Include a set of drawings to show you're serious. Some of the larger outfits will respond to this by pricing your building supplies by way of attracting your business. Think very carefully before jumping into this first price. Get another quote and then, once you've decided who to go with, get them to put in writing the discounts you've agreed on. The discount may vary according to the nature of the goods you're discussing.

Under this account-based system you or one of your authorised men gets something from the yard; they issue you with a docket there and then and the tax invoice comes later by post. You must keep this in your records (see page 156) for VAT purposes. Each month they'll send you a statement which they expect to be paid by the end of the following month. This could mean that if you were to buy something on day 2 of month one you'll in effect be paying for this item two months later. This can be very helpful indeed, especially when the financial going gets tough. It's the only way professional builders could hope to run a business. All accounts have a monthly credit limit. This could be anything from £1,000 to £5,000 but will obviously be much higher for a professional building company.

When obtaining a price from a merchant, always establish that you are actually going to do the job, not that you are just sounding out all and sundry for prices. Dealing with nice people also matters a lot. A merchant who will go the extra mile for you is worth paying a bit more for. I've even had good suppliers deliver stuff to me on their way home in their own car when I've been in a fix. This sort of service can save your life on occasions. This said, given the average 50% mark up in the building supplies business, everyone expects you to do a deal. Obviously, the larger your order for any one thing, the better the deal they can do. As I write this I am ordering materials for a large job and touting around for best prices on 400 sheets of a specialist building board. This order, worth several thousand pounds, is creating interest and will also certainly end up

'Are you sure this is cheaper than Bathstore?'

being supplied direct from the manufacturer to my site with a merchant taking his percentage for goods he'll never see. This is what they like.

The art of bargaining is a delicate one, as it is in any industry, because you won't want to alienate a good local supplier, yet you won't want to be ripped off either. As self-building becomes increasingly respectable, many merchants will give you good discounts. Don't be seduced into wasting lots of time searching around, though, trying to match what your main contractor can get things for. Almost all merchants have several discount levels and your man may be on the very best because of his high throughput and reliable track-record with them. This can often mean you're better off using your contractor rather than buying certain things yourself, even allowing for his mark-up. I've also found that it keeps main contractors sweet if they think you're allowing them into the purchasing loop so they can make that little extra profit. None of this bargaining and dealing happens with the DIY sheds.

A merchant who will go the extra mile for you is worth paying a bit more for

Whilst talking of the sheds, don't expect things to be all that cheap. And don't expect great service or information. What they are good for is basic stuff of various kinds, including finishes, but they can't usually compete on heavy-side items like sand, blocks, steels and so on. It's worth looking in the sheds for items that involve something more like shopping than bulk buying. Tiles, paints, lighting, even bathroom fittings and sanitary ware are all becoming more attractive and competitively priced in the sheds as the years go by. Obviously the sheds want you to pay there and then....there's no account trade unless you are a proper builder – and you'll pay extra for delivery.

There are new, up-and-coming businesses that specialise in supplying the self-build market. Two are: Buildplan and HousebuilderXL. Going with such outfits means you don't have to negotiate or haggle but you do end up with all your eggs in one basket. I suspect that in time there'll be even more innovative ways of sourcing materials when self-building.

As self-building becomes increasingly respectable, many merchants will give you good discounts

I look on page 156 at record-keeping and book-keeping but here let me say that just because you have an account with a supplier doesn't mean you can turn everything over to them and forget it. Quite the contrary. Expected (and promised) discounts may be 'forgotten' or genuinely omitted by a less than bright employee. As with so many things like this in life, errors always seem to favour the supplier!

Cutting out middle men

We all like to think we could get rid of the middle man and buy direct from the manufacturer. In some areas of life this is possible and even encouraged. In the world of building supplies it can, however, be fraught. First off, you'll need the skin of a rhinoceros to have the gall to get around the conventional supply chains that scratch each other's backs. A lot of this is very annoying and tedious and makes you wonder how such conditions can still exist in the modern, competitive, world. But they do and this is particularly true of specialist suppliers who, frankly, won't want to know you.

Some products can be obtained only through authorised dealers/suppliers. These manufacturers simply won't cut out the middle man, for anyone. In return, the suppliers give them loyalty and promote their goods. I find this too cosy and it really annoys me. Often, the result of the so-called loyalty and promotion don't provide a benefit to me, the customer. Other companies supply all and sundry, especially in the world of the Internet. This, understandably, doesn't go down well with builders' merchants. But this will increasingly be the way in the future as people become used to buying so many of their life needs direct and won't be bullied into other methods. Certain manufacturers may not want to deal direct with you but they may be happy to have your professionals do so. I get many things direct from manufacturers on behalf of my clients, even when I'm buying a one-off and may never purchase from the company again.

As this isn't a self-building book I won't go into detail about buying the many materials and supplies you'll need. If you employ a quantity surveyor to take off your bill of quantities (the shopping list of everything you'll need to build your place), he'll not only save some of his fee by showing you how to do things in the most cost-effective way but will have all kinds of great connections with suppliers. This could save you legwork and loads of time.

Your designer may also be able to get you in on the local supplies circuit. This sort of help is worth its weight in gold if you are new to an area or building for the first time. It's unrealistic to try to learn all these lessons (and get them right) on your first effort. Unashamedly ride on the backs of your professionals. You may never do this sort of project again but they surely will. For this reason, if for no other, suppliers will listen to them. You can benefit from this.

24 Visitors

Although you might have imagined that running a building site simply involved doing the actual building work and getting on with things, in reality there's a lot of other stuff going on, all of which will take you away from the construction process.

Over the duration of your build you'll have all manner of visitors. Early on there'll be friends and family all keen to see what you're up to. As work progresses all the professionals involved will come from time to time – sometimes several at the same time. There'll be statutory visits from Building Control Inspectors, and unwanted visit from reps, local 'inquisitives', and perhaps even the seriously unwanted criminal 'visitor'.

Early on there'll be friends and family all keen to see what you're up to

I've already looked at health and safety issues with regards to visitors. Anyone who comes on to your site must be protected from danger, whether they are invited or not. But, beyond this, how you handle visitors will differ depending on who they are.

Professionals may be glad of a cup of tea if you've both got the time and then get on with the work in hand; friends and relatives will want you to stop working, perhaps for ages, to take the grand tour. It can be hard to stay convivial at certain times, as Sod's law dictates that when they turn up you'll be in the middle of something really tricky or conflict-ridden! Of course this will simply confirm in their minds your madness for undertaking the project at all: but perhaps that's why they really came!

If you go through your diary every few days you'll be able to check whether you've done what you should

Whoever the visitor is, always enter the details in your diary. This is important but hard to adhere to if you don't get into the habit of doing it.

A simple entry such as: 'Peter (architect) came about leaking windows. Showed how to make temp repair. Decided to get rep in next week. He'll call him. Came 2.30 went 4.00.'

You'd be surprised how many people forget, or even deny, that they came to your site. This quasi-legal log can be a godsend if things go wrong. And they often do.

But as well as keeping a log for this purpose, a diary is even more valuable as a management tool. If you go through your diary every few days you'll be able to check whether you've done what you should. If the note about Peter's visit involved you in taking a certain action, you'll have this to add to your 'to do' list and it won't get forgotten. It's also an interesting management tool as it enables you to see who, in fact, does indeed do what they say they will.

Professionals may make several site visits in any one day to various clients, and then forget which client they promised what. Given that no one cares about your build more than you do, your record may be all there is.

25 Quality control

When we buy a TV, the snags have been ironed out and high levels of quality control applied throughout its manufacture. When we build a one-off house things couldn't be more different. I've already pointed out that all house building effectively takes place in a one-off, outdoor factory where quality is hard to control.

If you employ a good contractor he'll work to expected industry standards and hopefully higher, but even then things will need watching all the time because people make mistakes. If you employ subbies directly, your level of quality control and supervision will have to be that much higher. It's vital to seek professional guidance on this because you could so easily miss important things and because some tradesmen who see you're new to the job might be tempted to take short-cuts and perform less well because they hope they can get away with it.

The Tables over the next few pages should help you check for the most important quality issues as you go along. If ever in any doubt,

Daily action list

- Keep public roadway and footpaths clear of obstructions/damage/ soiling/rubbish
- Check excavations are safe
- Are safety barriers everywhere still effective?
- Are perimeter fencing and gates functioning properly?
- Clean up site and dispose of rubbish
- Re-route trailing electrical leads and cables
- Check skip isn't being abused by others
- Is site toilet in clean working order?
- Get food and drink as required
- Check that First Aid box and safety/protective equipment are where they should be
- Check scaffolding/other access systems are safe and not tampered with
- Look out for signs of theft/break-in (including plant still there)
- Check the safety of all stored/stacked materials (piles of timber/blocks etc)
- Look for signs of weather damage to materials or completed building work
- Write site diary
- Keep up financial day book
- Pay due invoices
- Chase 'to do' list and make new ones
- Check diary for day's meetings (on or off site)
- Check deliveries schedule

ask your builder or talk to an independent professional. Don't take chances.

When I'm building, whether or not I have a main contractor, I check everything in the following Tables (and more besides), just to be sure. In fairness, this sometimes annoys people because, by implication, it suggests they aren't doing what they should. However, this is one of many areas of self-building where you have to grow a thick skin. The way I see it, I'm not being critical, I'm exercising my responsibility as the final manager of the project to ensure that things are going how they should. I'm also very aware that it's my money that's being spent and my neck on the block when things go wrong.

If you employ subbies directly, your level of quality control and supervision will have to be that much higher

I'm exercising my responsibility as the final manager of the project to ensure that things are going how they should

You'll certainly get the odd negative glance as you go round checking things. A way round this is to do it at the end of each working day when the men have gone home. Now's the time to discover that your fireplace aperture is the wrong size, not when your insert won't fit three months from now and the brickies are off on another job.

Not only does this constant supervision give you confidence that things are being done how they should be, it'll also help you learn how the day-to-day elements of your build are actually done. Get out your textbooks, listen to your professionals and be as certain as you can that everything is being done properly.

Checking stage by stage

Site Clearance and Preparation

- Get insurances in place
- Take 'before' photos as evidence of what you started with
- Check roadway and public footpaths are not being soiled/damaged
- Check for damage to neighbouring property
- Use banksman (safety lookout man) when trucks are exiting to public road
- Keep records of truck (muck-away) movements, as it's easy for the company to charge for too many truck-loads
- Take down or mark overhead cables etc, for awareness
- Protect drains/water pipes from heavy traffic
- Clearly mark dangerous ground areas (boggy ground, pits, excavations)
- Toxic/dangerous waste to be taken to suitable sites only by appropriate contractors
- Save everything you could sell
- Mark and fence off protected trees/areas of garden and grounds to be saved
- Ensure there are no unauthorised fires
- Is site fencing/security in place?
- Get a secure container, if needed, for valuable salvaged materials pending sale
- Keep neighbours happy
- Install builders' electricity and water supplies

Groundwork and Foundations

- Are excavations safely marked?
- Keep excavations more than 1m deep properly shuttered
- Are the foundations marked out in the correct location on the site?
- Are the foundation dimensions correct (depth/width/length)?
- Measure from corner to corner diagonally in both directions to ensure dig is square
- Be certain trenches are clean/no visible roots/no muck in base
- Is access for ready-mix safe, and possible?
- Have you enough men available to manage the concrete pour?
- Is your vibrator ready? (if needed)
- Get plenty of covering material ready for when concrete is in place
- Check the deadwork is constructed to the correct height
- Is the oversite clean, compacted and weed-killed ready for ground floor slab pour?
- Have you enough men to do this?
- See that steel mesh for slab is raised off base 50mm before pour
- Prepare a laser, or similar kit, to ensure slab level
- Prepare plenty of protective materials to cover slab after pour
- Are the drains running in straight lines?
- Is there an inspection manhole at every direction change?
- Are the drain falls correct?
- Check that drain joints are all properly made
- All drain pipes should be laid in pea shingle below and above
- Is your cesspit or other off-mains system prepared?
- Trenches for services must be dug to appropriate depths (mains water 750mm, electricity 450mm, gas 375mm, telecoms 500mm). Use same trench if possible
- All service trenches to outlying places (shed/front gate/pool/garage etc) should be in place
- Use safety marker tape 150mm over all electricity cables during backfill
- Is the mains electricity cable coming to the correct place at the house for the mains consumer panel?
- Take photos of all trenches and their contents (including drains) before back-filling

External Walls

- Check the damp-proof course is in place (150mm above finished ground level)
- Are all airbricks (used only for suspended floors) clear?
- Check that blocks of the correct dimensions are being used
- Are the cavity trays properly installed? Get a professional to check early on and show you how to check in future
- Be vigilant that the cavity is being maintained (check for mortar bridges on wall ties – wash off at once to prevent bridges crossing cavity)
- Cavity insulation must be properly installed, tight to back of inner skin
- Check there are expansion gaps where needed (in long runs...every 6m for blockwork; 15m for brickwork)
- There should be no air gaps around items going through walls
- Check the positions of window and door openings
- Check dimensions of window and door openings
- Methodically check for plumb (vertical) and level (horizontal), especially of all door and window openings
- Check that bonding between blocks or bricks is complete (no gaps or voids in mortar)
- Monitor the quality and colour of mortar for finished brickwork
- Ensure no staining of bricks
- Fresh brickwork to be covered if rain, strong sun, or frost is due
- Check no damaged/chipped/cracked bricks or blocks are being used
- Rendered walls should be smooth, of consistent colour, and show no cracks
- Timber cladding should be consistent in quality, colour, and dimensions – and fitted securely

Roof

- Trusses should be equally spaced
- Check that the roof pitch is as designed
- Diagonal braces installed?
- Is the wall plate properly secured to top of inner masonry skin?
- Is the overhang distance correct?
- Sarking felt should have no holes/damage before battening is installed
- Battens must be in treated timber and fixed with rust-proof nails
- Roofing materials must be clean/ undamaged/uniform/properly fixed
- Check that lead work around the chimney is correctly installed
- Soakers and other lead work must be correct at junctions of roof and walls (get a professional to check this)
- Mortared ridge tiles should be properly bedded with no mortar staining down tiles/slates
- Insulation materials must be properly installed with a breather/ventilation gap when required (check with a professional)
- Loft space should be totally dark...with no daylight visible from indoors
- Check all roof penetrations for air and light-tightness
- Check that extractor outlets and vent pipes are all connected as they should be
- Take professional advice about how and if the loft should be ventilated
- Be sure the loft hatch is properly insulated with no air gaps around its edges
- Test the loft ladder carefully

Rainwater goods

- Check that guttering is in straight lines running to outlets (no sags)
- Ensure all clips are fitted properly
- Are all the joints waterproof? Test with a hose
- Be certain all downpipes are fitted to the wall at correct intervals and vertical
- Downpipes entering gullies must discharge water effectively
- Do you need leaf traps etc to be installed on gullies?
- Check in heavy rain how everything works
- Ensure roofing felt overhangs into the gutter
- Ensure tiles/slates overhang the gutter properly so rain falls into the gutter
- Make sure guttering is free from obstructions/debris
- Fit leaf protection for gutters in areas with heavy leaf fall

External windows/doors

- Ensure windows are as specified before being fitted
- Ensure directions of opening are correct before installing
- Check everything opens and closes as it should
- Check all parts (seals/trickle vents/ glazing beads or tapes, etc) are present
- Remove glazing labels
- Are the windows fitted correctly into openings...including checking cavity closers? Check with a professional for first one, then supervise the others yourself
- Check that reveals are the agreed depth
- Check all windows for plumb, level and square. Window openings should not be more than 8mm out of square
- Seal around frames, once fitted, to ensure air-tightness
- Protect glazed areas from future mortar or plaster damage by masking off temporarily with heavy-duty polythene
- Check external doors are as specified
- Be sure all draught-proofing is in place and functioning as designed
- Check level threshold (now required by law) is installed so no water comes in
- Once installed, a door should not swing on its own
- Keep keys (including spares) safe
- Be prepared to fit new locks once you move in as many people will probably have your keys supplied with the door

Glazing

- Look for scratches and imperfections from 2-3m away. Blemishes less than 25mm long are probably acceptable
- Listen to your professionals. All glass has some manufacturing imperfections and blemishes.

Internal doors

- Check doors are as specified before installing
- Look at each door for flatness/ blemishes (especially with pre-finished doors)
- Check door lining dimensions and strength before fitting doors
- Doors should hang in place and neither open nor shut on their own
- See that there are enough hinges per door (three or even four for fire doors)
- Are all the screws in every hinge?
- Hinges should not squeak or bind
- Door edges shouldn't bind to the frame. There should be an even gap of about 3-5mm all round
- Be careful how much clearance you leave under the door. Allow for the thickness of the finished floor surface so you won't have to remove the door and re-hang it
- Test all locks, latches and keys
- See each door fits snugly to its stops and the stops are the correct size for fire doors
- Architrave should be accurately mitred at corners and fixed tightly to the wall

Walls and ceilings

- No crack in plaster should be wider than 2mm. If any crack exceeds this, take professional advice
- Look in a good, oblique, light (use a 100watt lamp on a wander lead) to see that plastering is smooth. Small blemishes around fittings are acceptable
- Ceilings should be flat and smooth, with no signs of the underlying plasterboard joints or fixings
- Coving/skirting/dado should be fitted so joints are all-but invisible
- There should be no ridges of paint where roller edges have been
- All paintwork should look 'solid' with no show-through of underlying coats
- Skirting should be horizontal but can have up to 5mm gap between floor and bottom edge

Electrical

- Employ a properly registered contractor and rely on him to get it right. Building Control will also help ensure all this is done as it should be ('compliant').
- Check every light-switch faceplate and 13 amp socket plate is horizontal and that the screws are secure
- Go round every electrical appliance/ fitting and see that it works as it should (hobs, ovens, fridges, immersion heaters etc)
- Take a sliver of tissue paper or paper handkerchief and, holding it firmly between your fingers, check all extractor fans are pulling as they should
- Go round the house with a small lamp or similar household gadget and plug it into each socket to test it works
- With light bulbs in every ceiling fitting, ensure that all lighting works, including dimmers, where fitted
- Use a cigarette to test smoke detectors are working
- Use a hair dryer to see heat detectors are working
- Test the alarm system, ensure that essential people have the code. Organise back-up for when you're not around

Heating and plumbing

- Employ a properly qualified contractor and rely on him to get it right
- Run the central heating and with the help of your plumber, learn how to use the programmer. This can be a bit of a PhD! Write the instructions down and keep them somewhere safe
- Test room thermostats (stats)
- Make sure all radiators work and are hot over their whole surface
- Report noises in the hot water system to your plumber
- Make sure hot water comes out of every hot tap
- Adjust hot water temperature to what's comfortable for you (or get your plumber to do so and show you how to do it)
- Ensure that all shower thermostats work
- If there are loud gurgling sounds on emptying sinks or flushing loos, tell your plumber
- Go round loos and basins sniffing out any bad smells
- Work every plumbed fitting (showers, loos, baths, outside taps, etc) to check that they do what they should

Floors

- Check every floor is flat. Over a distance of 6m it should not be more than 4mm out of flat. More than 6m, it can be up to 20mm out and still be considered 'flat'. In all circumstances the floor surface should be smooth
- Timber floors should not squeak, boards should be tight against one another, and there should be a gap of at least 15mm around the edge (under the skirting) of the flooring. This allows for expansion
- Items such as floor ducting and electrical outlets should not protrude above the floor surface

Tiling and ceramics

- Ensure tiles are as specified before fitting
- Check no cracked, chipped or blemished tiles have been installed
- Some ceramics need to be installed in a particular orientation. Be sure to check this is happening before it's too late
- Grout lines should be straight and true and of equal width
- There should be no thin slivers of tile at the edges of floors or walls. Better 'planning' can almost always make these redundant
- Tile corners should not protrude anywhere on flat surfaces. All tiled surfaces should be completely smooth and flat when viewed in an oblique light
- Check vertical grout lines for plumb and others for level before grouting is done
- Grouting should be of consistent colour and smoothness and should fill all gaps, including those between floor and walls
- External corners should have special beads, or tiles should be mitred to produce an attractive edge
- Floor tiles must be laid on a sand and cement screed or, if on timber, on marine ply very securely fitted to a strong, immobile sub-floor
- All junctions between ceramics and sanitary ware should be sealed with bathroom-quality mastic

Stairs

- Check all risers are the same height (including that from the finished ground floor surface to the top of the first tread)
- Ensure all newel posts, banisters and handrails are secure and feel 'solid'
- No gap anywhere in balustrade or between spindles should be more than 100mm
- As you construct the stairwell, be certain you have enough headroom to use the stairs. It should be at least 2m
- Do everything you can to ensure there are no squeaks. If there are squeaks now, they'll be driving you mad in a year's time

Kitchen

- Check all appliances work properly
- Look under the sink for leaks, testing the drain by filling the sink and watching underneath for drips
- Ensure all worktops are fitted securely and joins are carefully done
- Check cabinets for plumb and level
- Do all the cabinets have backs?
- Check doors open properly and close flat
- Are the door fronts to integrated appliances fixed firmly to them?
- See that door hinges have all their screws in them
- Check all drawers for smooth running/closing
- Check the kick board is in place and fitted securely to the cabinet legs
- Be vigilant about tiling quality around faceplates and fittings
- There should be silicone sealing the junction between tiling and worktop
- Check the extractor fan works (see Electrical above)

26 Major causes of delay and how to manage or prevent them

Poor or incomplete design

I'm sorry to say this is a common cause of delays, and one that should be preventable. You'd think that by employing a skilled and trained professional there'd be no hiccoughs on the design. Alas, this is sometimes not the case. It isn't uncommon for an architect to design something that isn't buildable, or can be built only after a lot more detailed design work. This is tricky because you'll now find yourself in the middle of a battle. Your contractor will be frustrated because he knows what's drawn isn't working (and probably feels daft at not having picked it up before) and your designer will feel foolish if he's made a mistake and your builder is right. In my experience the best way of handling this is to get your builder on-side to see how the matter can be remedied in the simplest way. This can usually be sorted out, if only because he is committed to getting something to work. However, on occasions the matter is of structural importance and your builder won't want to carry the can for such a decision. The bottom line is that you've paid good money for a proper design that'll work. If necessary, go to a third party to get another opinion. Whatever you do, don't let this dispute slow you down more than absolutely necessary. It's easy to lose weeks over this sort of thing. Get a structural engineer in, if that's what's needed, and knock the problem on the head in a week. The way to prevent all this is to make sure that your contractor has gone through the drawings in detail and, if necessary, liaised with your designer to clarify things way before building starts. As you get more experienced you'll be able to foresee problems yourself before they start holding you up.

In an ideal world everything should be agreed and costed before anyone builds anything

Poor specification

I spend a lot of time specifying, so I'm sure you'll forgive me for making a fuss about this subject. People often ask me about the German kit houses that progress seamlessly from week to week, always come in on time and budget, and generally give everyone a nice, warm feel. The secret here is meticulous specification. When you enter into a contract with one of these companies you undertake to specify absolutely everything and never to change a thing. This means planning out all your exact furniture dimensions and positions for pictures and wall hangings, and much else besides. The company then undertakes to ensure that all your lighting sources, power points, and so on are exactly right for what you want. Every item that comprises the build, down to the last detail of a door hinge, is specified and signed off. Obviously this takes a lot of time but once done, it's done. Many such companies achieve all this in a three-day visit to their factory and showrooms by the clients. To anyone with the appropriate mind-set, and little personal time to devote to their project, this is a dream because they can hand over everything to the kit house company and get on with running their lives, safe in the knowledge that it'll all turn up on site exactly as planned. This is what they are paying for. And it is never a cheap route to go.

However, this method is, apparently, alien to the British way of thinking, as judged by the way most people say they want to work. The problem with specifying everything ahead of time, they claim, is that they can't then busk it as they go along....it gives them no flexibility to change their mind whenever they choose. And this endless potential for change is what they think they want.

This flexible approach may sound attractive but rest assured it'll be bad news to your bank manager because this degree of endless flexibility is an expensive luxury that only the very rich can afford. It appears to offer the ability to make 'organic' changes to the design or materials but this brings not just cost implications but a lot of pain. The problem with building is that changing one thing has knock-on effects that can seriously affect a lot of other things. Some of these may well already have been built by the time you decide you want to alter something. Builders are intrinsically averse to demolishing stuff they've just completed. And who can blame them? This sort of change can throw even a very good builder off his stride, start to think about punitive 'extras', and genuinely worry about the start date for his next job.

In an ideal world everything should be agreed and costed before anyone builds anything. This isn't just the counsel of perfection, it can be done. In my opinion it should be done on every new build. The only time it cannot stand up as the best model is with renovations and restorations. Here, the number of unknowables is usually so great that there's no option but to go the 'endless flexibility' route. And this is why such building work routinely costs at least 40% more than new-builds and can go to 200% more!

Appointing main contractor/subbies too late

I've looked on page 84 at finding a contractor. Once you've decided on your man, get him to give you the best estimate he can of how long it'll be until he's free to start on your build. His start date will then be in the contract. Good builders are always busy, so allow many months to find your contractor. The best can be fully booked for up to two years in advance, so the sooner you get cracking on this search the better.

Good builders are always busy, so allow many months to find your contractor

When appointing subbies, allow yourself lots of time too. OK, your chosen plumber may just have been let down on a job and suddenly find himself free, but it's unlikely. It's virtually impossible for me to give any actual times for this forward planning because things change so much according to the financial climate, time of year, size of your job, attractiveness of your job, how much a subbie wants to work with you, and so on. I usually talk to all the subbies I'm likely to want right at the start of the project once drawings are complete. I can then send them what they need, so they can look things through and come back to me with thoughts on their availability. If a given trade says they're booked up for, say, four months on a large job, they may suggest someone else who'll help you out. If you draw a blank at this stage you'll still have loads of time to find an alternative. Most good subbies are flattered to be asked a long time ahead, and indeed really good ones are booked up many weeks in advance. I get short with people who are angry when a good professional isn't available the minute they want them. They seem to think such tradesmen are sitting around waiting for the phone to ring. No one worth employing is in this position, unless there are exceptional circumstances in his life.

Bad weather

The weather in the British Isles is exceptionally changeable. This can make building a challenge. In countries that have a climate (as opposed to 'weather'!) builders can plan their work with some accuracy. In general, it makes sense to get all your groundwork done in good weather because mud can slow things down badly and working in wet ground is more dangerous. The only other weather-based goal is to try to get the roof done and the windows in before the winter. Once a building is weather-tight, indoor work can progress.

It makes sense to get all your groundwork done in good weather

If the weather is remarkable in any way, note it in your diary.

The reality is that bad weather actually reduces building speed quite dramatically. Winds mean that work at even quite modest heights cannot be undertaken; strong rain slows up or even halts brick and block-work; frost makes masonry work inadvisable and other work tedious (sand freezes, for example); serious rain floods trenches and basements; exterior painting can't be undertaken, perhaps for many weeks; and so on. But in addition to all these somewhat obvious setbacks, bad weather reduces site morale, and slows up the build as even the simplest task becomes hard work. Health and safety issues start to be a real concern if scaffold boards are icy; cold, wet hands work

It's possible to weather-proof your site to some extent. Here are a few tips:

- Keep all stored materials well protected
- Cover your sand pile if frost is expected
- Store cement and plaster indoors
- Keep your water supply pipe well lagged
- Keep large tarpaulins handy to cover susceptible areas, if necessary
- Fill trenches as soon as possible
- Keep a submersible pump handy to get you out of trouble (for example a flooded foundation trench)
- Have suitable coverings handy to place over new masonry, especially if it's freshly pointed. This can be important both in bad weather and on very sunny days. Have similar coverings available for laying over fresh concrete on fast-drying days (sun or wind)
- Construct parking areas and access roads from good quality hardcore so the slightest rain doesn't see everyone bogged down
- Keep mud and muck off the public highway and footpaths...these soiled areas become much more dangerous in bad weather
- Keep skips covered so they don't fill with rain
- Get rainwater goods in place and functioning as soon as you can so roofs don't drip and flood surfaces below
- Seal window openings with construction-quality polythene sheeting (allowing for adequate ventilation) to keep the inside dry and usable by your tradesmen
- Have somewhere your men can shelter from rain and cold. On a large site this could even mean somewhere they can change their clothes

less quickly; and cars and other plant get bogged down in mud. Even consulting a drawing is difficult in high winds and rain. All this means decisions can be made in haste and mistakes increase.

Letting problems escalate

A lot of 'psychology' goes on around the average building site. One of the main problems is denial. When you start off as a rookie project manager you'll probably find yourself wary of confronting problems, and especially problem workers. You won't be sufficiently sure of your knowledge and skills, and will thus tend to delay confronting issues, even once they become apparent to you. To be a bit depressing for a moment, the reality is that by the time you, as an inexperienced self-builder, become aware of a problem, things are going to be pretty far down the track because your early-warning radar won't be great. In the light of this, my advice is to confront matters at once rather than delaying or denying. Problems confronted early almost always get sorted out more easily.

The contrary argument is, as one of my witty guys put to me: 'Never do today anything that could be put off until tomorrow because it might not need doing tomorrow!' Of course he was teasing me about my forward planning. But lots of people run their whole lives like this. Frankly, I don't much mind how you do things off your site but you'll get into serious trouble if you adopt this attitude when self-building. And sometimes this behaviour will cost extra money, extra time, or even put men's health and safety at risk.

I know it'll be hard, on occasions, to speak up when you're not sure of yourself but you'll just have to find what it takes to be courageous, courteous and tactful, rather than letting things slip.

Bad workmanship

The problem you'll have here is deciding what is bad. On many building jobs there's quite a wide range of 'acceptable'. Knowing what these tolerances are when you're new to the job is difficult or impossible. Look at my Quality Control Guide on pages 175-181 to help you with this.

Here are some tips:

- The moment you think something isn't how it should be, say something
- Record your concerns in your Diary
- Raise the issue with your contractor, rather than his employees. He may, for example, have asked them to do something in a particular way to save time or money. You may also be seeing something at an interim stage and jump to conclusions that this is how it'll end up.

If you can't readily agree that something is done badly (you'll usually be able to sort matters out quickly and amicably), seek the input of an independent professional. Your designer will do in most cases. He can either put your mind at rest that what looks wrong to you is in fact all right; talk to the contractor or subbies on your behalf and come to a solution; or, at worst, tell you how to take things further. Don't just refuse to pay or you could find yourself in contractual trouble.

Falling out with your builder

This is obviously a serious issue that could cause considerable delay. The challenge is deciding what this falling out amounts to and how it has arisen. Do you find his personality difficult? Is his behaviour and thinking incompatible with yours as a self-builder? Is he regretting having taken the job on at all? Is it beyond his comfort zone, for some reason? Does he seem to have a problem with everyone, or has he simply taken against you? Has he under-priced the job so he feels insecure financially? Has he got a personal problem (for example, his marriage falling apart) which is affecting his life generally? And so on.

> **The challenge is deciding what this falling out amounts to and how it has arisen**

Again, this is where your designer could come in. Get him to talk to the builder one-on-one to discover what he sees as the issues that have made him fall out with you. Your professional could help the contractor understand your side of the story (act as a mediator), suggest other ways of working that would mean less contact with the contractor; or might agree that you chose the wrong man for the job and will now have to seek a replacement.

This last scenario is, in my experience, terribly rare. It's almost always possible to sit down quietly with your contractor, preferably off the site (go for a drink together, for example, after work or at the weekend) and talk things through. He may find you too cocky (telling him what to do/bossing him around); he might think you over-rule or question him in front of his men; you may take unilateral decisions that cost him money without first asking him; he may say you upset his men; or your constant changes of mind are driving him crazy; and so on. Just listen empathically (see page 16) and you won't go far wrong. If the very worst comes to the worst, get a solicitor to advise you how to get out of your contract. There should already be adequate provisions for this eventuality in place in the contract from day one. More likely, you could alter your

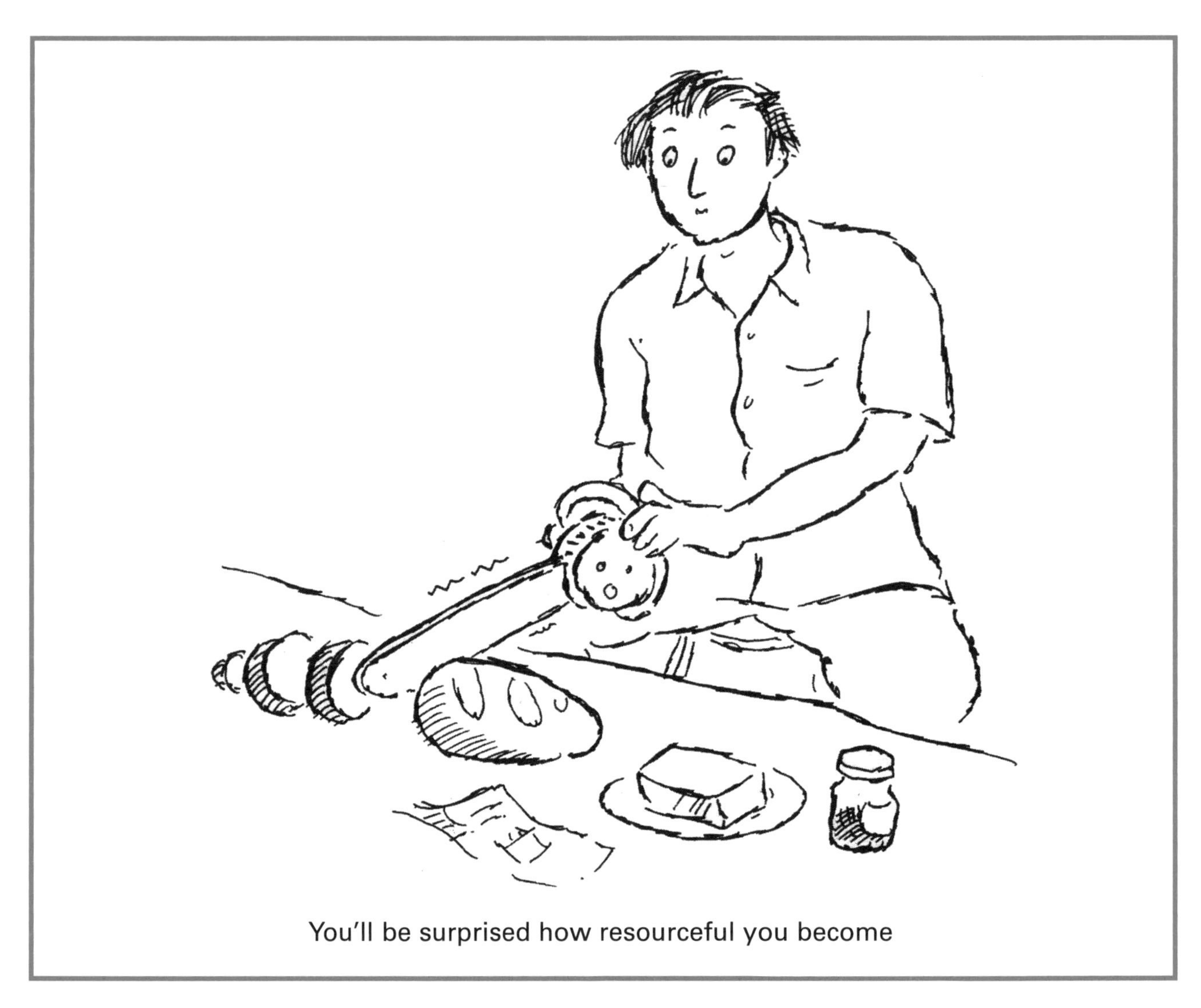

You'll be surprised how resourceful you become

attitude; your thinking; your management style, or whatever, to salvage something from the mess. Whatever happens, be sure to learn from the situation. I have found that such a confrontation of the issues often clears the air, creates a vastly better working environment, and makes the project go with a zing.

Falling out with your designer

I'm sorry to say this is more common than you'd imagine. Perhaps, in a way, it's surprising that it doesn't happen more often than it does. After all, you're inviting a total stranger into your life to help you create something you'll be living in for years and which will tie up most of your money. It will almost certainly be the most expensive thing you've ever bought. He will have his own ideas about how things should look or be done and you'll have yours. This creative tension can work really well when it works. When it does not, however, things can get nasty.

All professional bodies have a complaints procedure. The basic process is the same when dealing with any professional designer. Try to talk things through between you first, perhaps with someone there as a witness. Hopefully, the dispute will be settled there and then.

Apart from personality clashes (which can occur in any sphere of life), other areas that can cause friction between you and your designer can include:

- He takes on too much work and cannot give you the service you'd expected, or he contracted to supply
- You fall out over design issues on which he will not compromise
- He has designed something that cannot be built, as currently designed
- He finds you too hard to deal with because you constantly change your mind
- You refuse to pay him, or dispute his fees
- You perceive he has behaved unethically
- He finds you constantly second-guess him, making his job impossible
- Your lack of decision-making means he cannot work properly
- You instruct your builder to make changes behind his back (and he may end up being responsible for the changes)
- You withhold payment from him for matters that have nothing to do with him
- He feels you have lost trust in him
- You feel he should project manage the job but this is not what was agreed

Before setting up a meeting to talk things through:

- Look at your Appointment Agreement (the contract you signed with him)
- Remind yourself exactly what you agreed he would supply
- Clearly identify those parts that you think have not been met

If things are so bad that even this meeting cannot take place, contact the professional organisation to find out about their dispute resolution services. The Royal Institute of British Architects (RIBA) in the UK (and other professional bodies in their respective countries) has a very sophisticated system in place. The RIBA can, for example, nominate a mediator from their approved list. Go to www.architecture.com for lots more information.

'Unforeseens'

By definition, unforeseen issues cannot be foreseen. But this begs many questions. A highly experienced designer or contractor can see a lot more unforeseens than you'll be able to until you've done at least three or four self-builds. I look at causes for delays on pages 182-193. There'll always be certain areas of doubt and financial danger on any build. No one can see underground, for example. This means that trouble (expense and delay) can lurk there, however experienced you are.

Both designer and contractor should be entirely conversant with what you're trying to do

The way round unforeseens is to get your designer and contractor talking very early on, way before anything gets built. They are trained to look at predictable unforeseens, if you see what I mean. It's a matter of judgement and experience. If you've chosen the right contractor for a large renovation project, for example, his experience will alert him to all manner of what, to other even very good builders, would be considered unforeseens. This is where it's vital to choose the right horse for the right course when self-building. Both designer and contractor should be entirely conversant with what you're trying to do. There cannot be three parties all learning on your job!

Materials not available

This is a constant nightmare once you step off the tried-and-tested route of your local builders' merchant. Quite seriously, this is a very good reason for choosing materials and fittings that you can source locally. Sometimes even this can go wrong. Recently there was a shortage of cement in the whole building trade. Not even giant companies could get the amount they wanted. But this is unusual. Trouble with materials usually occurs when we buy non-standard items, especially from far-away places.

The only way I've found around this is to allow loads of time....and to allow for people misleading me over delivery dates. If a German window company quotes 8 weeks' deliver – allow twelve! If you are told your Indian limestone will take three months – allow five! And so on. Better create a storage problem than find yourself held up for a vital material or supply.

Materials supplied damaged/ wrong specification

This happens so frequently it could almost be said to be part of the building industry. I know colleagues who have exactly the same problems constructing international airport terminals! There is no answer to this because it's simply not possible to allow masses of time for everything to arrive on site in an unuseable state. It's a matter of discovering which suppliers tend to let you down the most and stopping using them.

Trouble with materials usually occurs when we buy non-standard items, especially from far-away places

Prevention is the best cure. Make sure everything is ordered in writing and copies kept on your files. When you know something is due for delivery, call the day before and double check they are bringing 'the 1800mm pink bath with three tap holes and all the panels to fit'. This is the time you'd be better off hearing, 'Jeeze guv, I swear you told me the red bath. It's already on the van'. At the very least you can cancel the plumber if they haven't got a pink bath in stock. All this thinking ahead will make your brain ache on busy days but it's one way of cutting down on the inefficiency.

Subbies, or your contractor, not turning up on site

Given that almost all builders and subbies are going to be working on your job alongside others at the same time, you'll find that people won't show up when you think you need them. This can be infuriating and drives many self-builders to distraction. But many such apparent delays may not in fact be so. Sometimes people don't show because they've thought things through and have decided they won't do their part of the work until Fred has completed his. They just haven't told you. Remember too that your contractor doesn't have to answer to you about his every move. All he has undertaken to do is complete your work in the time agreed. If he wants to, and can cope with building a multi-storey car park at the same time, that's his business!

When you know something is due for delivery, call the day before and double check

The emotional problem here is one of perception. Many self-builders get a bit possessive about 'their' builder and 'their' subbies. They create a nice working relationship, they argue, and then get pangs of sibling rivalry when they learn the main contractor has other 'children' to look after. Depending on your personality and your family-of-origin experiences, this sort of thing will concern you more or less. The facts are that as self-builders we can, indeed, become a bit obsessed with our job and can find it hard, or impossible, to accept that others aren't equally so. If you know yourself well enough to accept that this is an issue for you it might be sensible to employ a builder who will give you 100% of his time until your job is done. This can be a hard man to find but it can be done.

Your builder may also have perfectly good professional reasons for not coming that day. He may have decided to let your concrete go off for a while as he works elsewhere, for example. The odd day or two off shouldn't matter much unless a task is extremely time-sensitive. After, say, three days of a given subbie or your main contractor not showing, it makes sense to call them to see what's happening. I rarely find myself in this situation as, by creating good working relationships, few of my guys would dream of just not showing up without a call to let me know. It's worth doing whatever you can to create this kind of working relationship with your key people. This said, many even very good people who go into building work aren't the best of communicators. Most even very proficient and courteous subbies find themselves torn between various parties, all of whom assert their job is vital that day. An early lesson you'll learn is that good subbies aren't just in demand by you. They'll be courted by main contractors and will want, understandably, to keep these companies happy as they'll be giving them lots more work....long after you are gone and forgotten. If you were in their situation you'd do the same. But it's hard to be on the receiving end of this behaviour.

Keep a record in your diary of who's on site each day. If certain individuals or subbies have a contract with you, you'll be better placed to insist that they stick to it. However, many of the subbies you'll be hiring won't have gone this route and you'll feel aggrieved as they juggle you among their other jobs. Try to keep calm, listen empathically (see page 16) and make plans for alternative workers for when/if things go badly. If things start to go seriously wrong time-wise, it's vital to address the issue honestly with all concerned.

An early lesson you'll learn is that good subbies aren't just in demand by you

Illness

Anyone can get ill at any time. There's very little you can do to water-proof yourself against this. Keeping immaculate records is a good start so if you have to go into hospital, for example, someone else could see what's going on, pick up the build and keep things going. Running a site of any meaningful size means you must not keep everything in your head. If you were to be under the proverbial bus you simply cannot find your site grinding to halt because no one knows what's going on.

If you're doing the whole build yourself and fall off a ladder, then things will surely stop until you're well again. But this type of setback should be a rarity, and is yet another good reason for employing a contractor! Keeping your contactor in the picture at every stage is a good start in anticipation of your getting ill. Make sure related trades know each others' phone numbers so that in your absence they can still work on. Get good insurance.

Builder not paid

This is a sure way to bring your site to a halt. But it should never occur. You'll have agreed in your contract how and when he should be paid. Keep to this schedule immaculately and your contractor will go that extra mile for you, including waiting for his money when you cannot pay for a while, for reasons beyond your control. If you do find yourself in dispute, go back to your contract and see what was agreed. Get your designer to act as an intermediary and sort things out fast. Once your contractor leaves the site over a financial disagreement you'll be hard-pushed to get him back and will pay dearly to substitute him with someone else.

Legal problems

Hopefully, once you're under way you'll be free from legal nasties. Professional project managers in the construction industry in general spend a fair proportion of their time sorting out legal matters. Hopefully this fate will not befall you!

However, life has a way of getting tricky with building projects and there are several ways you could become embroiled in legal issues:

- Sacking your main contractor
- He sues you for unpaid monies
- Disputing payments to main, or other, contractors
- Neighbours take legal action for some reason
- Accident on the site, someone sues you
- You are fined by a regulatory body for contravening the law (e.g. ignoring listed building regulations)
- A supplier fails to honour their contract
- A workman sues you for negligence
- You sue your designer

And there are many more

Running a site of any meaningful size means you must not keep everything in your head

There's no point trying to be a DIY lawyer: seek legal advice at once and get matters cleared up. Impending law suits will not only cost you time, energy and money you can ill afford, they'll also dispirit you and slow your progress. Settle out of court whenever possible and don't allow matters to gear up.

Site closure

This is clearly a very serious 'delay'. You'll be very unlucky indeed to find yourself on the receiving end of this terrible event but it can occur if:

- You have a bad accident or even a fatality on the site involving a visitor, a trespasser or a member of your workforce
- If you are doing something the building regs inspector cannot sanction (or you're not complying with what Planning has allowed)
- Archaeological remains are found, that now need to be investigated
- Serious changes in ground conditions mean a complete re-design of your foundations
- Asbestos, or other noxious material, is discovered that has to be dealt with before anything else can proceed
- Your builder or you go bankrupt
- A critical supplier (such as of windows) cannot deliver for months more than they promised
- Your cash runs out
- You become seriously ill
- You fall out with your builder and have

to find another

- Your demolition work on a renovation project renders the place too dangerous. True, this might not mean total closure but things will grind to a near-halt.

I've looked throughout the book at these various subjects.

If you do find yourself in dispute, go back to your contract and see what was agreed

Not overlapping work ('sequencing') intelligently

It takes some considerable skill as a project manager to create schedules that enable work to progress in an overlapping way rather than end to end. Here are the parameters you'll need to understand in order to plan this:

- Make a list of all the tasks to be done in the order they need doing
- Ask each trade how long they'll take to complete them (including statements such as, 'I'll need to be there for one week once the stud walls are up, then come back once the plumbing is done, for another two weeks')
- Get out your drawings and, taking into account the geography of the site, plan who could be working at the same time as others yet not get in their way

Now create a list of tasks on a chart like the one on page 130. You'll see that all kinds of tasks are going on at the same time, though not necessarily even on the site. So while some people are making windows in Austria others are digging the driveway, others sourcing landscaping materials, others completing design tasks, you are raising the rest of the finance, and so on. If you were to build your project on a linear basis (with all the tasks end to end) it'd take years.

Be sure when allotting tasks to yourself that you don't overload things. You will not only be completing your personal tasks but also running the whole show, and this takes a lot of time. I reckon you should allow at least half your time to be taken up with management. This means that at best you'll have only half time to do actual building jobs – much as you may be itching to get on with them. Far too many self-builders get carried away with doing something they like (for example pointing a lovely old wall for two weeks) only to discover that all kinds of mayhem is going on behind their backs. Don't get seduced by personal hands-on activity when you should be tackling management tasks.

Be sure when allotting tasks to yourself that you don't overload things

This multi-level planning of activities is the main thrill of project management: playing the three-dimensional chess game that brings everything together at the right time in the right place and, hopefully, on budget. If this doesn't turn you on, think about getting someone else to do it.

Your designer makes changes

Frankly, there's little you can do about this unless you want a war. If he realises that something needs changing because he got it wrong, you can either get angry or settle down to sorting out the new work required. Hopefully the alterations won't set you back too much. He may, if the work is costly, agree to bear some, or even most, of the costs.

Your funding source won't release cash

This can be a chicken and egg story if you haven't completed enough work to convince your lender they should release that particular tranche of cash. Beg or borrow more money to get yourself off the hook, or throw yourself on the mercy of your contractor, until that work is done and your lender will pay up.

You have a personal/family crisis

This can be a real problem. Divorce, separation, a death in your close family, serious illness in someone close to you, losing your full-time job, money worries, and many other adverse life events can play havoc with your mental and emotional health and will slow you down. It's hard to plan for this, to be honest. When such things happen we all just try to survive day by day, perhaps looking to the build as a sort of therapy.

When you're feeling rough you're more likely to:

- Make mistakes
- Be short-tempered with your men
- Be tempted to take short-cuts
- Be sloppy about administrative tasks
- Forget key appointments or dates
- Lose concentration and cause, or be involved in, an accident

If you're really upset and don't feel safe, it's best to stay at home out of harm's way for a few days.

Unrealistic time-line in the first place

This is a common cause for delays. It's vital to be realistic in your original timings or you're bound to fail. Get your designer to go through the schedule with you and check what he thinks is sensible against what your contractor claims he'll achieve. If you're managing things yourself you must allow lots more time because you simply won't be experienced enough to make speedy progress. Be guided by your designer on how much longer to allow. Don't make the mistake of listening to people (especially eager and impatient family members) who tell you you'll be able to match the time of a contractor. You won't. He'll be more experienced; able to draft in extra men to get him out of a spot; and won't have to wait for trades to become available, like you will. He may also be able to throw cash and other resources at a problem rather than find himself held up on another, concurrent, job, or on his next job. If you're going to be doing much of the actual build yourself, as opposed to just project managing it, then double the time a contractor would take.

When starting out on a self-build, many of us underestimate the amount of time, energy and effort the project management side will take

This brings me to the realities of the time you'll, in fact, be able to offer the project. I hinted at this above. When starting out on a self-build, many of us underestimate the amount of time, energy and effort the project management side will take. If you intend to keep on your normal day job, or perhaps go part-time, then you could soon find there aren't enough hours in the day. Project managing a four-bedroom, detached house from start to finish (and I do not, of course, just mean the build) could take 2,000 hours of your time. The problem is that managing needs to be done when it has to be done, not when you happen to be free to do it! This is one of the major problems that self-managers come across unless they devote themselves to their build full-time. A couple of days with your eye off the ball could mean disastrous decisions being made by others, the outcomes of which will either be irretrievable or cost a small fortune to remedy. And all this because you thought you could manage the project on a part-time basis.

There's no rule of thumb I can offer about how 'big' big is, because you could take on a

It can help to take a break from the job

small extension that could be as complex and time-consuming as building a straightforward, detached family house from scratch. But in general I reckon it's impossible to project manage a new-build family home unless you are doing it nearly full-time. The exception to this would be if you have a fantastic contractor you have worked with before and whom you can trust like a brother. If in doubt, plan to put aside vastly more time than you'd thought likely, and you won't go far wrong.

As your build progresses, take stock of where you are on your time-line. Don't wait until you're way off before recognising (and admitting to yourself) that you have a problem. Once you realise that timing is slipping, seek your designer's opinion to see what could be done to claw time back. The secret now is to have the guts to get help. This could cost money but it's better to do this than to let things slip and then get depressed and even perhaps be unable to complete the build as things become desperate. Borrow more cash, call in favours, or reduce your expectations but keep the show moving forward. You'll be surprised how this can give you the kick you need to raise your spirits and get back on track.

Not anticipating delays

This is a sin you won't commit because you'll have read all this and come up with your own list of possible delays that are specific to your build.

Practical Completion

Strange to tell, it can be hard to know when your build is complete. Common sense says it's complete when what has been drawn and agreed on with the planners has been built. This is what your local planners and building regs inspectors will call 'completion'. In reality the issue is decided between the key parties, including the architect, the client, the building control inspector and the builder. At the other end of the scale is the zealous self-builder for whom the job is never complete!

This all becomes important if the final payment from your lending source can't be triggered until the right person says the place is 'complete'. Often, a self-builder desperately needs this money yet is on the horns of a dilemma because he really doesn't want to trigger 'completion' because other events start to cascade as soon as he does.

Snagging

Another problem with 'practical completion' as a concept is that your build may be habitable yet there could be many snags, or even some completely unfinished elements. Snags are details of the build that are incomplete or imperfect and that could reasonably be expected to be properly done before you take over the place to live in. Examples include doors that stick; poor quality paint finishes; a leaking sink; and so on.

Battles can occur now as you disagree with your builder on whether things are complete or not. He'll be keen to get his money (a chunk of his profit is embedded in this final payment) while you may fear he'll walk off to another job, leaving you with quality problems or items that aren't done at all.

> **Common sense says your project is complete when what has been drawn and agreed on with the planners has been built**

It's accepted as perfectly reasonable in the building industry for the client to retain two-and-a-half to five percent of the build cost against snagging and other final bits and pieces but this won't, of course, cover anything at all major that's left undone. There should be a Defects Liability Period in your contract with your builder. This usually means he has up to, say, six months to put things right, at which time he is due the rest of his money. Your architect will usually be a sensible arbitrator on this. He'll have seen it all dozens of times before and will advise you when to create a fuss and when to back down.

Of course if you are the builder you won't have this problem. Your main priority now will be to get your architect to certify that things are complete so you can get your hands on the final payment. This will mean him applying to the council for a Completion Certificate.

As you'll have learned by the time you get to this stage of your build, quality can be hard to assess in the real world of building. When we buy a new car we can be pretty sure that all the snagging has been done by the manufacturer, and we have come to expect very high standards from all manufactured goods.

But when we build a house, or have it built for us, small things are left undone, or actually develop after they have been built. They all need attention but aren't serious enough to say the building isn't complete. Yet they can be annoying and can even plague the whole project.

It's important to bear in mind that even very high quality professional building companies leave many scores of snags when they hand over a house

It's important to bear in mind that even very high quality professional building companies

Having the place professionally cleaned before moving in can make all the difference

leave many scores of snags when they hand over a house. The worst leave hundreds. I once bought a top-end apartment built by a first-class developer. Before we moved in they had two competent men working flat-out at snagging for two weeks! Most self-builders don't allow nearly enough time for this vital phase of the job.

The secret is not to let any snags get you down or spoil your enjoyment of your build

This is all somewhat paradoxical because what we are aiming for as self-builders is our dream home where any snags at all would seem unacceptable....far more so than if we were to have bought a spec house from a developer (whom we expect to get some things wrong). But this isn't reasonable because you're bound to have snags. The secret is not to let them get you down or spoil your enjoyment of your build. Make a plan to rectify the worst snags before you move in and then, perhaps some months later, go round with your cumulative list and have a blitz on those and any new ones that have appeared. I think this is better than continuously finding fault with your build quality and driving the family mad as you forever fuss and tinker with things. OK, it's technically become your home rather than a building site but your family will want a real home....not a low-level continuation of your build.

In 1999 the NHBC produced a Consistent Guide to Finishes in an effort to define what's acceptable and what isn't. As you can imagine, it's a minefield. How do you rate a scratch on a pane of glass? How much inconsistency of mortar colour do you tolerate over a large wall area? And so on. Building being what it is, it's probably fair to say that perfection is for the gods. The sensible individual doesn't even try to seek it. Also, believe me when I say that what seems like a real horror at first can soon become unnoticeable as you live in the place. Most of us building our own home are pretty hard task-masters and make a fuss about things that almost no one else would bother about (or even see!).

Of course everything to do with the structure itself has to be right but imperfections in fittings and finishes are probably not worth losing sleep over. My motto here is: 'Don't make perfection the enemy of the good.'

I think it's worthwhile asking an architect or surveyor to go round the completed job to do a snagging list. Not many self-builders do this but it can save a lot of heart-ache. When self-building, we tend to get too close to the project but an independent professional can take a more reasoned view. He'll also, frankly, be able to pick up things you will not, unless you are very experienced. Although you may think you've managed the perfect build, this will almost certainly not be the case. I find that a fresh eye can, for very little money, not only give a sense of proportion to the job but also pick up things I've missed. This is worth a lot to me, even with all my experience.

'Don't make perfection the enemy of the good'

VAT

As I pointed out on page 161, now is the time to get your VAT claim in. This must be made within three months of your completion date. The processing takes only a couple of weeks or so and you should get your money within a month. You may now suddenly feel rich, after ages of feeling poor. Be careful though. You'll be very lucky indeed if all this cash can be put into new toys for your home. Go through all your suppliers' statements, chase those that are outstanding, make sure every bill is paid, and so on. If you've borrowed from family, consider using this cash windfall to pay off some debts. You have, after all, only been bank-rolling the government by being a VAT collector! It isn't like winning the lottery. This said, if there really is money free, take the opportunity to buy something nice for yourself, do something for the garden, or even take a holiday as a present for your hard work.

Tying up loose ends

Now you're on the cusp of transforming your building site into your home, it's time to:

- Sell your temporary site accommodation if you bought something
- Get your own house sold (though you'll have started this process some months before)
- Organise removals
- Get things out of store
- Sell any tools and plant you won't need
- Sell, or otherwise dispose of, excess building materials. A local builder might want them; an ad in the local paper might get rid of them; auction them on eBay; or you could find a good cause locally that's doing some building and give them away
- Tell all the utilities and your insurance broker that the place is no longer a building site but your home
- Change any locks for which other people have keys
- Set up your alarm company
- Get a fire extinguisher, and a fire blanket for the kitchen
- Get the whole place professionally cleaned, including all the glazing (or do it yourself, if you have the time)
- Tie up loose financial ends with your accountant
- Check with your solicitor that all the legal issues are water-tight
- Check with your lender that everything's how they want it
- Have a party for the neighbours as a 'thank you' for their patience and understanding. They'll be delighted to take a look around your place
- Have the place valued, to give you a warm feel

Congratulations

You've finished! What a relief. Make time to take pride in this achievement. Try not to go around the project finding fault and wishing you'd done things differently. Let go. You've done something really special. Something very few people you know will ever do. Enjoy the finishing touches you spent so long perfecting. Take a pride in showing friends and family round. Try to avoid telling everyone about the faults....they'll just want to see the fruits of your labour. People also enjoy hearing how you overcame adversity in various situations. And your before and after pictures will be a source of delight to many – if only to convince themselves they wouldn't ever do anything similar.

It can be hard to make the transition from your site being a workplace for so long, to seeing it as your home. Hopefully your family will keep you grounded in this respect. This said, don't get dispirited when others take things for granted that you have spat blood over for so long. The build was, after all, *your* adventure, not *theirs*. All they want is a result. Most of us who self-build have to find our rewards deep within us.

How did you enjoy the process? Would you do it again? Will you do it again? Could it even become a way of making a living? What does your family think about the adventure? Bear in mind that if this is your first build you'll see dramatic changes in the way you do things next time. Once you've done three or four new-builds you'll have it licked!

As you quietly take stock I'm certain you'll find you've grown hugely as a result of your build. You'll have undergone considerable transformations in ways you could never have expected. Take a joy in these new skills and insights. No one can take them away from you. Delight in them and see how they could enrich your life and those around you in ways that have nothing to do with your build.

Index